# OUR PLACE
# IN THE UNIVERSE

# OUR PLACE IN THE UNIVERSE

*A Metaphysical Discussion*

J. J. C. Smart

Basil Blackwell

Copyright © J. J. C. Smart 1989

First published 1989

Basil Blackwell Ltd
108 Cowley Road, Oxford, OX4 1JF, UK

Basil Blackwell Inc.
432 Park Avenue South, Suite 1503
New York, NY 10016, USA

*British Library Cataloguing in Publication Data*

Smart, J. J. C. (John Jamieson Carswell), *1920–*
  Our place in the universe: a metaphysical
  discussion.
  1. Metaphysics
  I. Title
  110

ISBN 0–631–16777–3

*Library of Congress Cataloging in Publication Data*

Smart, J. J. C. (John Jamieson Carswell),
  1920–
  Our place in the universe.

  Includes index.
  1. Metaphysics. 2. Man. I. Title.
BD111.S57    1989        110        88–7963
ISBN 0–631–16777–3

Typeset in 11 on 13pt Garamond
by Hope Services
Printed in Great Britain

*To Thomas and Jessica*

# Contents

# Preface

This book is a revised version of my Gavin David Young Lectures at the University of Adelaide in 1987. These lectures were public lectures and consequently this book is designed for the general reader. Nowadays philosophy is a more technical subject than it used to be, partly because of the influence of modern mathematical logic, linguistics and the special sciences. However, I have endeavoured to keep these technicalities to a minimum. Since I believe that there is a continuity between science and metaphysics the book contains some 'popular science'. I have avoided mathematical formulae beyond the simplest. I have occasionally tried to explain certain mathematical ideas, but informally and sometimes with the aid of diagrams. I have not burdened the argument with defences against possible attacks by all sorts of differently minded philosophers. That way lies unreadability. I have endeavoured to give my own views about metaphysics and our place in the universe. It is necessary to make it clear that the matters that I deal with are controversial, so that there is no general agreement on them among good philosophers. This of course is a normal feature of philosophy. In philosophy anything can be questioned, including one's own philosophical methodology. Thus this book should not be read as one would an introductory book on chemistry, for example. I do not expect all (or even most) readers to be convinced by my arguments, and if any who are unconvinced or who dislike my conclusions are provoked to go on to explore the views of other philosophers I shall be very happy. Some alternative views can be got by following up the suggestions for further reading at the end of each chapter. With a good many exceptions I have tried to keep these suggestions to works accessible to the general reader. After all, some 'general readers' are more 'general' than others, and so though I hope that all or nearly all of this book will be accessible to readers with little scientific background, I expect that many readers, perhaps with some scientific and mathematical background, will like to have somewhat stronger fare recommended to them. I also incorporate bibliographical references to works mentioned in the text. This will allow me to avoid burdening the text with footnotes.

I should like to thank Jeremy Butterfield for commenting on the pages in chapter 3 concerned with quantum mechanics, John Pateman for commenting on chapter 4, John Leslie for commenting on chapter 7, Kai Hahlweg for discussing with me some questions to do with the reducibility or otherwise of chemistry to physics, and Philip Pettit for some comments on chapter 2. I must thank the co-ordinator and deputy co-ordinator of the Automated Reasoning Project, Research School of Social Sciences, the Australian National University, for having me with them as visiting fellow after my retirement, and Barbara Schmitzer and Jenny Pirie, of the Project, for word processing my manuscript.

# 1

# Introduction

We may conceive of metaphysics as the philosophical study of the universe and our place in it, the word 'place' being taken in both literal and metaphorical senses.

## LITERAL

We are inhabitants of a medium-sized planet of a medium-sized and very typical star (a 'main sequence' star) of a fairly typical galaxy of stars. Our galaxy has the common sort of flattish spiral structure. (An elliptic structure is also common, and a smallish minority have an irregular structure, as is the case with the two Magellanic clouds, which in the southern hemisphere are visible to the naked eye.) If we could see our galaxy from the outside and from a suitable position we would see the spiral structure. Our sun is probably situated on one of the spiral arms, rather far out towards the edge of the spiral structure. When we see the Milky Way we are looking within the flattish structure. The milky effect is due to the vastly greater number of stars in the line of sight when we look in this direction rather than in some other direction. (The word 'galaxy' is in fact derived from the Greek for 'milk'.) Our galaxy is supposed to have a diameter of 60,000 light years. (In other words, a light wave would take 60,000 years to traverse such a diameter.) Our galaxy forms part of the local group of about thirty galaxies of which ours is probably on the edge.

A well-known member of this local group is the great nebula in Andromeda, which is a galaxy similar to our own, and though 2 million light years from us is fairly visible to the naked eye in the northern hemisphere if there is no atmospheric or light pollution. The universe is expanding: the various groups of galaxies are rushing away from one another much as the dots on a rubber balloon that was being inflated and thus stretched would move away from one another. The further apart the dots the greater would be their mutual speed of recession. (It is not as if any particular dot or group of galaxies was being singled out for ostracism!) If a galaxy is sufficiently far from us it must be receding from us with a velocity greater than that of light and so no radiation from it could ever reach us. The telescopic images from the furthest galaxies are very faint, and light from them will have taken something like 10,000 million years to reach us, and so in observing them we are looking very far back in time as well as far away in space. There are probably something of the order of at least a hundred million galaxies within the range from which light can reach us. In every direction there are distant galaxies and clusters of galaxies. This distribution used to be thought to be quite even in all directions, though the distribution of *visible* galaxies is not so. (Correction has to be made for the obscuring effect of dust clouds in and near the direction of the Milky Way.) However, recent discoveries and conjectures about a 'great attractor' – perhaps a vastly larger conglomeration of galaxies – beyond the region of the known galaxies have suggested that the galaxies are not distributed as homogeneously as was thought. The law of mutual recession of the galaxies has to be supplemented on account of superimposed motions towards the great attractor. In particular our local group of galaxies has been discovered to have a velocity in the region of 600 km per second with respect to an absolute frame of reference defined by the isotropy of the cosmic background radiation, the residue of the 'big bang' when the expansion of the universe began.

It can be seen that our location in the universe is in no way an important looking or central one. Indeed there is no central place, unless we can think as such of the place in time of the 'big bang' from which the expansion and evolution of the universe is supposed to have begun.

Emotionally we can be daunted by these vast astronomical distances and numbers. In relation to time also we can come to feel our apparent insignificance. Where our forefathers thought that the age of the universe was a matter of only a few thousand years, we can trace the big bang back to a date something of the order of 10,000 million years ago.

The observable galaxies are thick on a map of the sky much as the individually visible stars are thick on a star map. Yet since the geocentric hypothesis of Ptolemy and Aristotle was abandoned even the sight of the stars has filled people with a sense of awe and a feeling of insignificance. Furthermore, in chapter 7 I shall refer to speculations that what we think of as our own 'universe' is but one of many such entities. It is hard today to recapture the state of mind of our forefathers who believed that humans had a privileged place in the universe, or that the universe was created especially for humans. Nevertheless, when we think of the vast astronomical spaces we can feel not wholly unsympathetic to Pascal when he wrote in his *Pensées* of the terror that was caused in him by 'the eternal silence of these infinite spaces'. For some the sense of loneliness in a vast unfeeling universe may be mitigated if it is believed that many stars in our galaxy have planets and that some of these planets would be suitable for the evolution of life, and that in a proportion of these again the evolutionary process would have led to the existence of intelligent life, so that the distribution of intelligent life through our galaxy might be quite high. If we accept the probability estimates of some of the theorists who have speculated on these lines we may of course feel some chagrin that the human species is not (so far as intelligence is concerned) 'the only pebble on the beach'. On the other hand, we may feel a nobler emotion, and may comfort ourselves by the consideration that even if we destroy all life on earth by nuclear holocaust the torch of life and intelligence will be carried on elsewhere. A chilling possibility is that all civilizations, terrestrial and extra-terrestrial, destroy themselves by nuclear holocaust as soon as they reach our present stage of technological sophistication. This is sometimes put forward as an explanation of why we have not received messages or observed explorers from other regions of our galaxy. The pace of technological advance is huge on a cosmic scale: on cosmic measures of time it is but a twinkling of an eye since *homo sapiens* evolved. Thus we would expect some planets to contain intelligent species whose technology would have passed far beyond ours and who could be expected to have communicated with us. A common explanation of why we have (at least at the time of writing!) not detected any such messages is in terms of the vast distances involved. Moreover, if we did receive an intelligible radio message from a star even only 100 light years distant, a fruitful dialogue with the extra-terrestrial originators of it would be difficult, as it would take 200 years to receive an answer to a question.

On the other hand, John D. Barrow and Frank J. Tipler have argued that we may be alone in our galaxy. Their argument depends partly on an evaluation of the possibilities of a sequence of lucky accidents that would be needed for life and then intelligence to have evolved in a given region. The argument is supported by the fact that we have not received extra-terrestrial messages or observed any visitors from outer space. Barrow and Tipler believe that we will soon be able to make self-reproducing intelligent robots (which they call 'von Neumann probes', in allusion to a paper by the great mathematician J. von Neumann which showed the abstract possibility of a self-replicating computer). These intelligent robots would not only replicate themselves but would design even more intelligent robots, and so on. Many of them would swarm into outer space, and without the ecological constraints that prevent even the population of rabbits reaching an astronomical number, they would colonize the galaxy. If one such robot replicated itself twice, using natural materials abundant in the galaxy, and each of these replicas replicated itself twice, and so on, through forty generations, then there would be quite a few for each star of our galaxy. If they could travel at a quarter of the speed of light they could reach the most distant stars of our galaxy in a quarter of a million years, a small period in geological time. Thus if intelligent life were common in our galaxy we could expect some of it to have originated long enough ago for us to have received news of it. Nevertheless, even if it were unlikely that there was more than one instance of intelligent life in our galaxy, we could expect it to be thinly spread over the universe at large. In view of the high (possibly infinite?) number of galaxies, intelligent life, though uncommon in any single galaxy, could nevertheless occur many (possibly infinitely many?) times in the total universe.

I shall return to cosmological issues in chapter 7. They raise questions of considerable philosophical interest. I do not draw a sharp line between philosophy and science. Philosophers have traditionally been concerned with metaphysics, which is theorizing about the nature of the universe. Most of our present ideas about the universe come from science rather than from philosophy as traditionally conceived. I think of much of theoretical science as philosophical in nature because it deals with deep conceptual questions. Not all science does, however. Thus organic chemistry, for example, is difficult, requires great ingenuity and flair, but nevertheless is not highly conceptual in the way that philosophy is or the cutting edge of theoretical physics is.

I hesitate to give a definition of philosophy, because the nature of philosophy is something controversial and something on which philosophers disagree. What philosophy is or should be is itself a philosophical question. That is why, perhaps as a result of the university upheavals in the late 1960s and early 1970s, some philosophy departments have given courses in fringe topics which to others of us do not seem to be properly located in philosophy departments. This sort of thing would not happen in chemistry departments, because chemists agree on what is and is not chemistry in a way in which philosophers do not agree on what is and is not philosophy. In place of a definition of philosophy I shall simply point to what are traditionally regarded as philosophical writings from Plato (or even some of the pre-Socratics) onwards, and to what typically goes on in philosophy departments of universities.

Some *caveats* are needed: for example, in the eighteenth century the word 'philosophy' meant much the same as our word 'science'. (The *Philosophical Magazine* is a physics journal, in Oxford there is a chemistry chair of 'Experimental Philosophy' and in Scottish universities 'Natural Philosophy' means applied mathematics and theoretical physics.) On the other hand, many of the writings that many contemporary people think of as philosophy (such as Parisian café philosophy) I might be tempted to classify as literature or political theory. Coming nearer to a definition, I would say that philosophy is argumentative discourse, but then so is science, history, law and other subjects. I should also say that it is typically concerned with conceptual questions. Let me give an example of a conceptual question, one to which I shall return in chapter 5. Suppose that you get a glimpse of a Dalmatian dog (plum pudding dog). The dog is white with a definite number of black spots on it. But does it make sense to say that your glimpse has a definite number of black spots? *If so* perhaps you should be able to tell us how many. But *if not* could anything in the world have an indefinite number of anything? There are a lot of muddles, deep conceptual confusions, that need to be sorted out, in the way in which this question has been put. Experiments in psychological laboratories will not help.

Theoretical physics produces a lot of conceptual problems. Newton and Einstein should be thought of as great philosophers as well as great physicists. It used to be said, rather arrogantly by some philosophers, that in their systems of metaphysics they produce new concepts that may be taken over and put in more testable form by scientists. I am inclined to say that the boot is on the other foot: that the best contemporary theoretical physicists are far more conceptually innovative and imaginative than are professional philosophers. Nevertheless, there are philosophical questions that philosophers, in virtue of their upbringing, are usually better equipped to discuss than are scientists. For example, there are subtleties about notions such as those of 'reality' and 'truth' and of the 'mental' and the 'physical' where even the best and most conceptually innovative of scientists can usefully expect help from those officially called 'philosophers'.

SEMI-LITERAL

From the literal sense of 'place in the universe', as that of inhabitants of a medium-sized planet of a fairly typical star in a fairly typical galaxy, I passed rather insensibly to the question of whether intelligent life is unique, rare or common in the galaxy or the cosmos itself. This suggests another sense of 'our place in the universe' which I hesitate to classify either as literal or as metaphorical and so will call 'semi-literal'. This is the sense in which one might talk of a person's place in a hierarchy or of a hen's place in a pecking order. (This semi-literal sense of 'place' comes together with the literal one at those dinner parties where guests are seated according to their rank.)

Earlier I mentioned Pascal's remark that the vast astronomical spaces terrified him. However, in the same fragment of the *Pensées* Pascal goes on to comfort himself with the thought that the whole dignity of humanity consists in thought, so that 'if the universe were to crush him, man would still be nobler than his destroyer, because he knows that he dies . . . but the universe knows nothing of this.' On this criterion we are nobler than even the largest and most brilliant star. Are we nobler than the great nebula in

Andromeda? On Pascal's criterion perhaps yes, though perhaps not if somewhere in the great nebula in Andromeda there is intelligent life. If God exists then of course on Pascal's criterion God is (where he should be) highest in the hierarchy because he is omniscient.

About fifty years ago it was quite a common view among astronomers that there was probably no other intelligent life in the universe, or in our galaxy at least. Thus one (no longer generally accepted) theory of the origin of the earth and other planets was that they arose as a result of the near approach of another star to the Sun. Such an event was thought to be so improbable that it could not be expected to have occurred elsewhere. (My father, who was an astronomer, liked trespassing and once when we were crossing a Scottish moor he remarked that just as stars never came near one another so we were unlikely to encounter a gamekeeper!) Cosmologists now tend to suppose that planets originated in a different manner, so that very many stars could be expected to possess planets suitable for the emergence of life and eventually of intelligence. Nowadays belief in this is strong enough for the effort at present being made (with huge and very sensitive radio telescopes) to receive radio signals from outer space.

As I have already noted, the cosmologists Barrow and Tipler take a more sceptical view. They are impressed by the fact that evolution of intelligent life is the result of a sequence of highly improbable events and circumstances. If I may be allowed to stylize the matter in a rather artificial way, suppose that for life to exist on a suitable planet of a given star there must be a sequence of ten events, each with a probability of one divided by 10,000. Then the probability of life existing on the given planet would be $(1/10^4)^{10} = 1/10^{40}$. Since the number of stars in our galaxy is of the order of $10^{11}$ it would follow that even if every star had the same chance as our Sun of possessing a planet suitable for life, which is very far from being the case, the chance of life elsewhere in our galaxy would be of the order of $1/10^{30}$ which is near enough to zero. (John Buchan's adventure novels illustrate this sort of point.

He had a great literary skill and a confident way with coincidences which makes us suspend disbelief, but really it ought to make it impossible to regard many of his plots as credible. They depend on sequences of remarkable coincidences, each of which is perhaps believable, but the whole sequence is as near as makes no difference impossible.)

If very sensitive radio telescopes, with complicated computers to separate out faint signals from the surrounding electronic 'noise', do succeed in detecting signals from intelligent beings on a planet of a distant star, this will surely have a great emotional effect on human beings, much as (or perhaps even more than) was caused by the Copernican and Darwinian revolutions. If signals sent out with the low power of our present radio and television broadcasts were detectable, it is likely that any signals in reply would come from beings scientifically and technologically far in advance of us. The last generation or two are the first to have sent radio signals from our planet, and a couple of generations cover a miniscule span in evolutionary time. This consideration raises a queer thought. Suppose intelligent life from a planet fifty light years away has detected our immediately post-war television signals. Perhaps a return signal from them is on the way, or perhaps again they are on the way to look at us. (If they are able to travel at a quarter the speed of light most of the way we could not expect them for another couple of hundred years.)

Intelligent signals from outer space would presumably be in a coded language with devices to enable us to break the code and discover the language. (Ways in which this might be done have been investigated by H. Freudenthal.) Would this contact be as disruptive for terrestrial civilization as the advent of white culture to American Indian or Australian Aboriginal society? Probably not – at least a mere radio contact would not lead to the transmission of disease. The intellectual community might be upset if superior beings exploded (by arguments that were amazingly novel but obviously cogent) some of our most cherished philosophical and theological prejudices. As against this, the existence of fundamentalist religion, 'creation science', and so on in the midst of an advanced scientific civilization, and which even uses advanced scientific technology to disseminate its propaganda, surely shows the ability of at least some humans to shut out new ideas from consciousness.

The disturbance caused by receiving messages from superior extra-terrestrial intelligences would be less than it would have been if we had been able to engage in easy dialogue with them, but, as I have remarked earlier, dialogue by means of radio transmission would be a very slow process. The discovery of superior extra-terrestrial intelligences could of course be felt as a great blow to human vanity, as indeed would be the invention of super-intelligent machines on earth. In western thought there has been a tendency of human beings to think of themselves as (below God) the highest form of life.

It is true, of course, that Christian thought has included belief in angels, but the supposed encounters with angels have never been described as telling us anything very exciting intellectually, for example how to produce a unified theory of the four forces of nature, or how to prove or disprove Fermat's last theorem (a simply stated proposition in number theory to which no exception has been found and yet which has so far been recalcitrant to proof). The superiority of angels seems to have resided mainly in their possession of wings and some skill in playing the harp. According to some Christian thinking all shall be revealed to us after death (cf. I Corinthians 13. 12), though this may refer not to intellectual achievement but to a direct personal relationship with God of a sort not obtainable in this life. I have sometimes wondered why those Christian philosophers and scientists who did seem to believe that intellectual illumination would come to them after death did not abandon their toilsome earthly inquiries and hasten the event by shooting themselves! Perhaps their belief was not a genuine one. David Hume has remarked that most Christians, even while professing belief in a heavenly after life, nevertheless from their behaviour show that they regard death as a great evil.

Christianity is a very anthropocentric religion, because according to it God became man. Judaism and Islam are in their own ways somewhat anthropocentric too, but no such charge could be laid against Hinduism and Buddhism. Few Christian theologians seem to have concerned themselves with the question of the relation of the doctrine of the Incarnation to the possibility of intelligent life elsewhere in the universe. C. S. Lewis addressed the problem when he suggested in his novel *Perelandra* that terrestrials might be the only ones to have sinned, but if life is very common elsewhere this solution is an extremely unplausible one. Indeed on an evolutionary perspective original sin seems a certainty: since we have evolved from animals suited to different environments, very many of our emotional responses will be inappropriate to our present situation. Thus combativeness may have been useful for early humans but it is a very dangerous trait in an age of nuclear weapons. Be that as it may, it would be very odd if terrestrials were the only ones to have sinned. It is perhaps more plausible theologically to interpret the doctrine of the Trinity in such a way that the Second Person could be multiply incarnated on many planets. E. L. Mascall has explored this possibility.

The possibility of life elsewhere in the universe is not of course the only blow to humans. As I mentioned earlier, so were the Copernican revolution and the theory of evolution. Vanity surely lies behind the unreasonable opposition to the theory of evolution on the part, even today, of certain evangelical sects and churches. Even those who fear that they may be consigned to hell by a wrathful God will feel also that this shows them to be important in the scheme of things, in that even the creator of the universe takes an interest in their deeds and misdeeds. Nevertheless, one must agree that vanity is not always a prop to religious belief: at the other extreme, religion can of course also appeal to feelings of submissiveness.

It should be conceded also that there is in western tradition an important divergence from thinking of humanity as the acme of creation. There is the striking doctrine of 'The Great Chain of Being', about which the philosopher and historian of ideas A. O. Lovejoy wrote an important book of that title. The idea has been traced back at least as far as Plato's *Timaeus*. It forms a major theme of Pope's *Essay on Man*, and its prevalence in western thought to some extent offsets the streak of human egotism to which I have drawn attention. Pope places *homo sapiens* (as well perhaps as intelligent beings on other planets) in a salient but nevertheless modest position – the most earthy of spiritual beings and the most spiritual of earthy beings. This leads me to a third sense in which the words 'our place in the universe' might be taken – a metaphorical one.

### METAPHORICAL

Metaphorically, reflection on our place in the universe can be reflection on whether or not human nature is or is not totally explicable by science, whether we are at least partly spiritual or whether we are just complicated physical mechanisms, whether the world around us is really as science pictures it to us or whether it is in whole or part illusory or else mind dependent, and so on. In this context we may raise questions about the human mind. Is the mind identical with the brain? Or is it rather a soul that could exist quite apart from the brain? Or is it something in between? Is the material world merely a lot of actual (and perhaps possible) ideas in our minds or in God's mind (as Bishop Berkeley held)? Is the mind essentially a unit or is it merely a congeries of perceptions and ideas, as Berkeley in his *Commonplace Book* dared to suppose but was too fearful to pursue the matter? He wrote: 'Mind is a congeries of perceptions. Take away the perceptions and you take away the mind. Put the perceptions and you put the mind.' Such questions about the mind were discussed many years ago in C. D. Broad's now rather dated but deservedly well-known book *The Mind and its Place in Nature* whose title illustrates the metaphorical use of the word 'place' with which I am concerned at present.

Some of these issues can be highly emotional because they impinge on human hopes and aspirations. Thus it may be thought that idealism, the view that everything in the universe is in some sense mind dependent, may be more conducive to aspirations to immortality and communion with a Deity than is realism, the doctrine that the universe at large is in no sense mind dependent (or perhaps that the universe is not at all mind dependent *except* for having been created by a spiritual being – God – outside the universe).

The word 'idealism' is of course both ambiguous and vague. One use of the word 'idealism' should be set aside at the outset as irrelevant to present concerns. This is the ethical sense in which we may describe a person as concerned with good causes. There is no reason why a metaphysical realist should not be an idealist in this sense. Again 'idealist' is sometimes used pejoratively to indicate that a person may have too rosy a view of human nature. Once more there is no reason why a metaphysical realist should not be prone to this rather likeable defect, if defect it is.

Leaving such irrelevant uses of the word 'idealist' aside, let me refer to an important distinction, that between 'subjective idealism' and 'absolute idealism'. Subjective idealism is typified by the theory of Bishop Berkeley, who held that talk about physical objects is talk about ideas in our mind or in God's mind. A Berkeleyan idea can be either a sense impression, such as a yellow patch in my visual field, or else a mental image which is a copy of a sense impression or a complex made up out of such copies. (In fact in chapter 5 I shall cast doubt on the existence of sense impressions or mental images or Berkeleyan ideas, and on the clarity of notions such as is implied by the phrase 'yellow patch in my visual field'.) Thus according to Berkeley the world consists entirely of minds (or 'spirits') and ideas. Berkeley relegates talk about theoretical entities (in our day he would have given the example of 'electrons', 'protons', etc.) to the instrumental, merely an algorithmic device for getting from meaningful statements about ideas of sense to other meaningful statements about ideas of sense. In our time certain physicists have espoused an account of scientific theories rather similar to Berkeley's, and so Berkeley's metaphysics should in no way be regarded as a mere historical curiosity.

A different sort of idealism is the 'absolute idealism' whose greatest British exponent was F. H. Bradley. According to this tradition also, though in a different way, the world that we investigate in scientific inquiry is not independent of mind. (Though by 'mind' here is meant something other than the object of empirical psychology.) The tradition of absolute idealism really goes back to Immanuel Kant, who held that there are certain 'categories' or structural forms of organization that we impose upon the world presented to us in sense experience. The mind independent world of 'things in themselves', the so-called 'noumenal world', was held by Kant to be unknowable. According to Kant all we know are 'phenomena'. Phenomena here are not to be thought of as subjective like Berkeleyan ideas, but as objective in the sense that they are independent of particular minds and are that on which scientific investigation converges.

Recently Hilary Putnam has produced arguments, different in nature from Kant's, but in the same general tradition, and I shall discuss Kant and Putnam in chapter 8. If these arguments are correct they have a considerable bearing on the metaphorical interpretation of the phrase 'our place in the universe', since they give a picture of a world that is bathed in our own mentality. Putnam has summed up his position (also rather metaphorically), in the preface to his book *Reason, Truth and History*, as the view that 'the mind and the world jointly make up the mind and the world' and 'the Universe makes up the Universe – with minds – collectively – playing a special role in the making up'. Such a view implies that science does not give us even an approximation to ultimate metaphysical truth. Putnam has castigated the sort of approach which I am taking in the present book as 'scientism'. Certainly if either Kant's or Putnam's views are correct I am not justified in treating metaphysics and science as continuous with one another. Quite apart from their own intrinsic interest, it is therefore important for me to discuss Kant's and Putnam's contentions. I shall do this in chapter 8.

Not only because in the literal sense of 'place' our place in the universe is somewhere in space or time, or more properly (as I shall suggest) in space-time, but also because in my opinion seeing physical objects (including persons) as four-dimensional space-time entities often furnishes a clue to solving various philosophical problems, I shall in the next chapter discuss the space-time manifold and how motion is represented in connection with it.

### SUGGESTIONS FOR FURTHER READING AND BIBLIOGRAPHICAL REFERENCES

Useful introductory books on metaphysics are Keith Campbell, *Metaphysics: an introduction* (Encino and Belmont, Calif.: Dickenson, 1976), and Richard Taylor, *Metaphysics*, 2nd edn (Englewood Cliffs, NJ: Prentice-Hall, 1974). For more on my own view of the nature of philosophy, see J. J. C. Smart, 'My Semantic Ascents and Descents', in Charles J. Bontempo and S. Jack Odell, *The Owl of Minerva: philosophers on philosophy* (New York: McGraw-Hill, 1975), and reprinted in J. J. C. Smart, *Essays Metaphysical and Moral* (Oxford: Basil Blackwell, 1987). A brief and elementary introduction to Berkeley, which has the merit of treating him as a philosopher of science, is J. O. Urmson, *Berkeley* (Oxford: Oxford University Press, 1982). An elementary introduction to Kant's philosophy is Roger Scruton, *Kant* (Oxford: Oxford University Press, 1982). Both of these are in the Oxford Past Masters series. For F. H. Bradley see Richard Wollheim, *F. H. Bradley* (Harmondsworth: Penguin, 1959). The questions from Blaise Pascal in the text are from his *Pensées*, edited by Louis Lafuma and translated by John Warrington, with an introduction by H. T. Barnwell (London: Dent, 1973), Fragment 392. The remark by Hume mentioned above will be found in his *Treatise on Human Nature*, book I, part 1, section 9.

Other references are as follows: John D. Barrow and Frank J. Tipler, *The Anthropic Principle in Cosmology* (Oxford: Clarendon Press 1986); H. Freudenthal, *Lincos: design of a language for cosmic intercourse*, part I (Amsterdam: North-Holland, 1960); C. S. Lewis, *Perelandra: a novel* (London: Bodley Head, 1967); E. L. Mascall, *Christian Theology and Natural Science* (London: Longmans Green, 1957); A. O. Lovejoy, *The Great Chain of Being: a study of the history of an idea* (Cambridge, Mass.: Harvard University Press, 1948); C. D. Broad, *The Mind and its Place in Nature* (London: Kegan Paul, 1925); Hilary Putnam, *Reason, Truth and History* (Cambridge: Cambridge University Press, 1981). The quotation from Berkeley in the text is from his *Commonplace Book* in A. C. Fraser (ed.), *The Works of George Berkeley* (Oxford: Clarendon Press, 1901), vol. I, pp. 27–8. For evidence about peculiar motions of the galaxies, over and above the mutual recession due to the general cosmic expansion, and for conjectures about the 'great attractor', see Alan Dressler, 'The Large Scale Streaming of Galaxies', *Scientific American*, September 1987, pp. 38–46.

# 2

# Space-Time

The first of the three senses of 'Our Place in the Universe' that were distinguished in the previous chapter was the literal one. It is a matter of our place on Earth in relation to Sun, stars, galaxies, and perhaps beyond. All these, it may be said, are situated in space and time. In this chapter I want to argue for thinking not in terms of space and time taken separately, but in terms of a single entity, space-time.

We commonly say that space has three dimensions and that things such as stars, mountains, footballs and rabbits have three dimensions too. For example, we can talk of north and south, east and west, and up and down. However, is this quite right? Stars, mountains, footballs and rabbits endure through time. Should we not say that they therefore have *four* dimensions? Similarly we can say that one part of space is at one time occupied by a ship and that the same part of space is at another time occupied by an iceberg. Should we not say therefore that space itself endures through time? Should we not say, then, that space itself has four dimensions? Or rather, should we not speak of space-time, not of space and time taken separately? If we do, then, we think of the space that at one time is occupied by a ship and at another time is occupied by an iceberg as distinct entities, distinct temporal stages of a four-dimensional chunk of space-time.

This is made clear in figure 1. Since I have only two

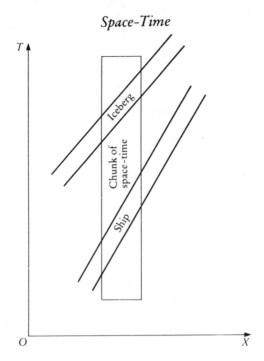

*Figure 1*   Relative velocities of a ship and an iceberg

dimensions to play with on the paper I can draw only one space direction if I am to leave room for the time direction. (Actually the surface of the paper endures through time and so it really has three dimensions, two space ones and one time one, but let us forget this or alternatively think of figure 1 as it is at an instant.) Let *OX* be a space direction (say due north) and let *OT* be a time direction. (It will shortly become clear why I say 'a' and not 'the' time direction.) Allowing for the fact that I have drawn only one space dimension in figure 1, the figure shows a chunk of space-time (corresponding to our common sense notion of 'the same place') and suitable temporal stages of the ship and iceberg of the previous paragraph.

The figure uses unnatural units of space and time, because if I used more natural units (according to which the velocity of light would be unity) the chunk of space-time, the ship and iceberg would be represented by exceedingly thin lines, at such small inclinations to one another as to be visually indistinguishable. Thus light travels at 186,300 miles per second. So in the natural units one second of time would be equal to 186,300 miles. Again, the nearest star is four light years away – the distance light travels in four years. So in the natural units the distance of the nearest star would be the same as is four years. In considering the theory of relativity shortly I shall say why unity is the natural unit for the velocity of light, but in any case the choice of the number one does seem to be a non-arbitrary one if we have to choose a finite number greater than zero. (The velocity of light is obviously not zero, nor is it infinite since light takes time to travel from one place to another.) On the scale of figure 1 relative velocities (in the *OX* direction) of ship and iceberg are shown by their different inclinations to one another, and their velocities relative to the chunk of space-time are shown by their inclinations to the vertical. I shall leave in abeyance just for the moment the question of whether we can consider space-time as 'absolute', in which case the chunk of space-time will be part of the furniture of the world, or whether it is 'relational', a construction out of relations between space-time things and events.

Some will resist this four-dimensional way of looking at things. They may object that according to this view we would never see (say) a tomato, because the tomato, as four-dimensional entity, would extend into past and future. However, I see no difficulty in saying that we can see something that extends into past and future. We can see a tomato, and what we say we see has back and interior as well as a facing surface. To see a tomato is roughly to be reliably caused by our eyes and visual system (as well as by an external stimulus, the reflection of light from the object into our eyes) to come to believe that there is a tomato before us. Of course vision is not infallible: I may merely seem to see because what is before me is only a shiny red hemispherical artefact, and not a tomato at all. In which case I merely seem to see a tomato. Similarly the tomato might miraculously have come into existence and might soon miraculously vanish. It might have no past or future to speak of. But to say that all I see is an instantaneous 'time slice' of a tomato would be too sceptical, analogous to saying that I see only the surface of the tomato, not the tomato itself. I see the tomato as internally succulent and also as enduring. (That is what I am reliably caused to believe.) Of course the reliability is not perfect. The tomato may conceivably exist only instantaneously, just as it may inexplicably vanish or the red shiny surface belong to a fake tomato. Alternatively if you want to say that you do not really see a tomato (an object extending into the past and future) but only an instantaneous 'time slice' of it, then in consistency you should say that you never see tomatoes but only their facing surfaces. For the concerns of this chapter I do not mind much which way you go here, though I have a personal preference for the less sceptical locution, but if you go one way about the tomato and its back and interior then you should go the same way with the past and future of the tomato.

Some philosophers will indeed insist that when you see the tomato you see the whole tomato, not just an instantaneous time slice of the tomato. They will resist, however, the idea that 'the whole tomato' is a four-dimensional object. D. H. Mellor has been insistent that 'the whole object' is present at an instant. Even apart from the colloquial sense of 'Are you all there?' querying mental aberration on someone's part, it would indeed be odd of me if I were to deny that I was 'all there' at the present instant. If I did it would perhaps be taken to suggest that I had lost a leg or an arm. But in metaphysical contexts I think that I can illuminatingly say that not all of me is here right now.

Suppose that a signal light changes from red to green. I contend that this means that a later temporal stage of the light is green and that a temporally adjacent stage of it is red. (I use 'is' and 'changes' in the previous sentence tenselessly, like the 'is' in 'Two plus two is four.') Mellor would say that the *whole* signal light is red at $t_1$ and green at $t_2$. I can say that the whole signal light is the four-dimensional object that is the signal light from its construction to its destruction and to say that it is red at $t_1$ and green at $t_2$ is just to say that a temporal stage of it that is at (or around) $t_1$ is red and that a temporal stage of it that is at (or around) $t_2$ is green. Let us also consider change of belief. If Jim changes from believing that whales are fish to believing that whales are mammals, it is one temporal stage of him that believes the one thing and another temporal stage of him that believes the other thing. Mellor, P. T. Geach and other philosophers have protested against this way of talking. I agree that it is odd, and not elegant English, but I fail to see what is wrong with it, indeed I fail to see what the metaphysical difference is supposed to be between 'The whole thing $S$ is $P$ at $t$' and 'The temporal stage at $t$ of the whole thing $S$ is $P$', though there is indeed a difference in colloquial elegance. I here construe 'the whole thing $S$' as referring to a four-dimensional space-time entity. I can even construe 'The whole of me is here now' (e.g. I have no arms or legs missing) as 'The here–now temporal stage of me is whole' (e.g. there are no here–now temporal stages of arms or legs missing).

### THE SPECIAL THEORY OF RELATIVITY

I suggest then that even common sense can be construed as having an underlying four-dimensional view of the world, even though it does talk of an enduring space and a non-enduring time. Talk explicitly in terms of space-time is clearer. But if I am wrong about this, then common sense should yield to science, because the notion of space-time is absolutely central to the special and general theories of relativity. The special theory of relativity is Einstein's early (1905) theory. The general theory is Einstein's later theory which is designed to give a geometrical explanation of gravity. The general theory reduces approximately to the special theory when it is applied far from the vicinity of heavy bodies.

Many popularizations of the special theory of relativity make use of mythology of such things as clocks and railway trains moving past one another, or of light rays being reflected back from distant stars. This seems to me to be an artificial and misleading way of looking at the matter. A more natural and illuminating way is to consider a certain disharmony between Newton's mechanics and Maxwell's electromagnetic theory, the twin pillars of nineteenth-century physics. The dynamical laws of Newtonian mechanics retain their form if they are expressed relative to different frames of geometrical axes that are moving with uniform velocity relative to one another, and if one uses the commonsensical Galilean transformations. Consider rectangular axes $OX$, $OY$, $OZ$ and a point $P$ (figure 2). Then if the distance of $P$ from the $OY$, $OZ$ plane is $x$, the distance of $P$ from the $OZ$, $OX$ plane is $y$ and the distance of $P$ from the $OX$, $OY$ plane is $z$, then the ordered triple of numbers $(x, y, z)$ are the 'co-ordinates' of $P$, i.e. they fix its position. Thus if one set of axes $(O'X', O'Y', O'Z')$ is moving with velocity $v$ along a common axis $OX$ $(OX')$ with respect to the other $(OX, OY, OZ)$ then if $x = 0$ when $t = 0$, then $x' = x - vt$. In this case we also have $y = y'$, $z = z'$ and $t = t'$, in transforming from $(x, y, z, t)$ to $(x', y', z', t')$. To make Maxwell's equations retain their form we need a different set of transformations, the Lorentz transformations:

$$x' = \frac{x - vt}{\sqrt{\left(1 - \frac{v^2}{c^2}\right)}}, y' = y, z' = z, t' = \frac{t - \frac{v}{c^2}x}{\sqrt{\left(1 - \frac{v^2}{c^2}\right)}}$$

where $c$ is the velocity of light. (If we take measures of space and time so that this is unity, the terms $c^2$ can be omitted.) The Lorentz transformations look paradoxical to common sense. In particular they imply that however fast we chase a

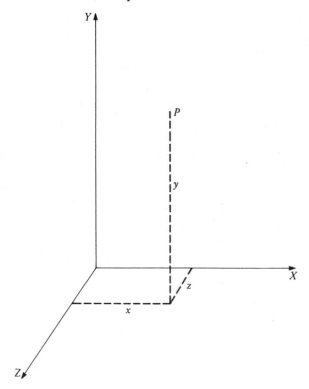

*Figure 2*  Axes and co-ordinates

light wave, it will always move away from us at the same velocity. However, I shall indicate shortly that the Lorentz transformations have their own sort of antecedent beauty and naturalness which the Galilean transformations lack. To explain this I need to explain the idea of a transformation which is due to a rotation of axes.

Consider a pair of two dimensional axes $OX$, $OY$ and $O'X'$, $O'Y'$ where the lines $OX$ and $O'X'$ coincide but $O'$ lies a distance $a$ on $OX$ away from $O$ (figure 3). In the $O'X'$, $O'Y'$ system the co-ordinates will be $x' = x - a, y' = y$. This is a transformation of *translation* of axes. Suppose now that instead of moving $O$ to $O'$ we leave $O'$ as coinciding with $O$ but *rotate* the axes at a certain angle, so as to give axes as in figure 4. Then the transformation from $(x, y)$ to $(x', y')$ will be slightly more complicated. Those who know a little trigonometry will easily write it down.

Now let us go back to the Galilean transformations that left Newtonian dynamics invariant. Einstein, in his epoch-making paper 'On the Electrodynamics of Moving Bodies' (1905), chose to keep Maxwell's equations intact by replacing the Galilean transformations by the Lorentz ones, and by modifying Newton's mechanics so as to make the laws of dynamics invariant under the Lorentz transformations.

In the case of bodies moving at ordinary velocities, for example those of rifle bullets or even of planets moving around the Sun, the new equations of dynamics gave the same observable results as the Newtonian ones did. However, at velocities nearer to the speed of light, as with particles

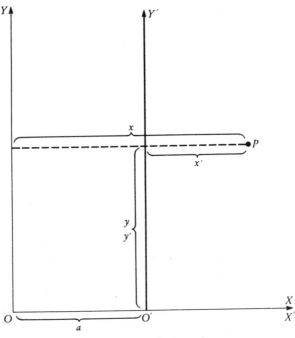

*Figure 3*    Translation of axes

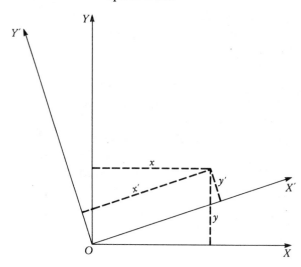

*Figure 4* Rotation of axes

accelerated to high velocities in cyclotrons, the predictions of
the new mechanics have been very different and have been
amply confirmed by experiment. Indeed one might say that
they have even been confirmed by engineering, since these
relativistic effects have to be taken into account in the very
design of a cyclotron.

For my present philosophical purposes, however, the date
on which I wish to lay especial stress is 1908, when
H. Minkowski gave his beautiful address 'Space and Time' in
which he showed that the Lorentz transformations can be
seen as a rotation of axes in space-time. He made the
hypothesis that the geometry of space-time is a sort of hybrid
between the familiar Euclidean geometry of most people's
schooldays and a certain sort of non-Euclidean geometry.
Thus we can call the geometry of space-time 'semi-Euclidean'.
Consider rectangular axes *OX, OY, OZ, OT* in space–time,
*OT* being a time direction. Consider light rays passing
through *O*. If we take units of space and time so that the
velocity of light is unity, the light rays will all be at an angle of

45° (half a right angle) to *OT*. Thus the light rays through *O* all lie on a double cone, a 'light cone'. Ignoring *OY* and *OZ*, the light cone is drawn in figure 5. Since no known particle can be accelerated beyond the speed of light, world lines of material particles (the lines along which as four-dimensional objects these particles lie) are all within a light cone. If a particle had 'imaginary mass' – e.g. so many grammes multiplied by the square root of minus one – then its world line would be entirely *outside* a light cone. Such a particle would need a force to accelerate it from an initially greater than light velocity *down* towards the velocity of light. The

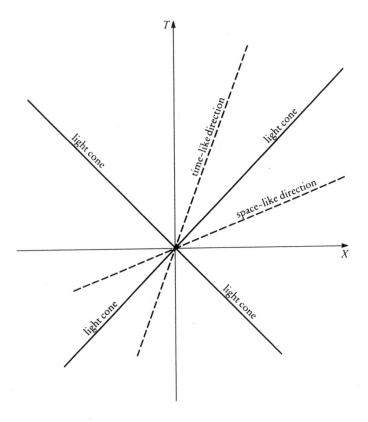

*Figure 5*　Light cone

word 'tachyon' has been coined in order to describe such faster than light particles with imaginary mass. No such particles have been detected, and so we can suppose that every world line of a particle with positive mass lies entirely within some double light cone. (Photons, particles of light, lie *on* a light cone, since they have zero mass.) However, I do not think that there is any obvious *absurdity* in the notion of a tachyon itself, at least on account of the notion of imaginary mass, because mathematicians have shown how to make the concept of an imaginary number (e.g. the square root of minus one) completely respectable. Indeed the term 'imaginary', though hallowed by tradition, is quite misleading.

Lines that lie entirely within some light cone are called 'time-like'. Those that lie entirely outside some light cone are called 'space-like'. Consider now a right angled triangle *ABC* where the right angle is at *B* and *AC* is the hypoteneuse, and where *AB*, *BC*, *AC* all lie in space-like directions. Since Minkowski's geometry is Euclidean in space-like directions we can apply Pythagoras' theorem, and so $AC^2 = AB^2 + BC^2$. Consider now a right angled triangle *ABC* where *AC* is the hypoteneuse and such that *AC* and *AB* are time-like. In this case, because the geometry in time-like directions is a certain sort of non-Euclidean geometry, we have $AC^2 = AB^2 - BC^2$. The geometry of space-time is like Euclidean geometry except for some minus signs.

Consider two material bodies in constant relative motion to one another and to a set of axes (which in special relativity are taken to be inertial axes, i.e. axes relative to which a body not acted on by any force lies along a straight line in space-time). The velocity of one body relative to another is simply related to the angle between the world lines of the two bodies. Two bodies at rest with respect to one another lie along parallel world lines. It can be seen that in the space-time pictures of Minkowski's theory, motion is simply a matter of relative inclination of world lines. This will be important when I shortly come to consider what seems to me to be the muddled idea that time flows.

Minkowski's geometrical explanation of the kinematics of special relativity makes the latter seem almost obvious. It can be seen to have an antecedent plausibility that the Newtonian kinematics lacks. For example, if we represent Newtonian kinematics in four dimensions, it is still natural to take a person's time axis along that person's world line. If he or she has a clock handy, the clock's world line will be parallel to (or almost along) his or her world line. But if we rotate a time axis, should we not equally rotate a space axis? Rotating a time axis without rotating any space axis seems arbitrary, mathematically ugly. Thus as Minkowski said in his already mentioned paper, the Lorentz group of transformations is 'mathematically more intelligible' than the Galilean group. I have suggested that even in pre-relativity days there was a philosophical case for thinking of the world as four-dimensional. How much more is this the case since Minkowski's beautiful interpretation of special relativity. Minkowski said: 'Henceforth space by itself and time by itself are doomed to fade away into mere shadows, and only a kind of union of the two will preserve an independent reality.'

The power of the Minkowski explanation of the Lorentz transformations as being simply a rotation of axes in space–time can be illustrated if we consider the so-called 'twin paradox'. In figure 6, $OS$ is (near enough) the world line of twin Peter who is shot off in a space ship (travelling at constant velocity nearly all the way) to a distant star whose world line is $S'SS''$ and whose vicinity he reaches at $S$. He is then shot off in a similar way back to Earth to rejoin his stay-at-home twin Paul at $A$. (Actually there should be little curves on Peter's world line at $O$, $S$ and $A$ to indicate his periods of acceleration and deceleration. However, these can be supposed to be small compared with the distances $OS$ and $SA$ and we can ignore them. A more complex calculation could indeed take them into account without altering the result.) Since $OS$ and $SA$ are time-like the geometry of figure 6 is a certain sort of non-Euclidean geometry, and in this geometry $OS + SA$ is *less* than $OA$. This is as in Euclidean geometry

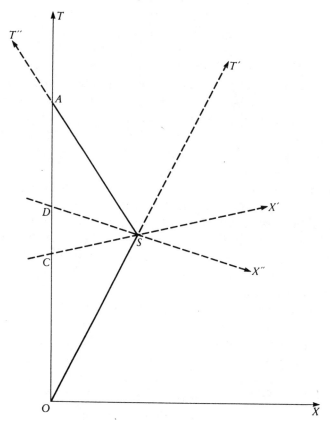

*Figure 6* Twin paradox (so-called)

except for the 'less than' instead of 'greater than', and derives from the already mentioned minus sign in the equivalent of Pythagoras' theorem. Admittedly it does not look like this in figure 6 because I perforce draw the figure on a Euclidean piece of paper. Similarly the upward inclination of $OX'$ and the backwards inclination of $OX''$ do not look right for a rotation of axes, but once more this is because a figure in non-Euclidean space has been drawn on a Euclidean sheet of paper. (If $OS$ had been the world line of a photon then $SX'$ and $ST'$ would have indeed come together to coincide.)

Allowing for these obstacles to intuition, it becomes quite obvious from the figure that Peter will be younger than Paul when they meet again. (Distance along a world line is the same as increase of age, because each person will take his time axis along his own world line, according to axes with respect to which he or she is at rest.) The same result could have been got according to the mathematics of Einstein's 1905 paper by means of an easy but tedious calculation, but Minkowski's geometry gives us a simple explanation and an intuitive sense of clarity and obviousness.

Some have sensed paradox because if we consider Peter as at rest Paul will have gone away and returned to Peter. So Paul should be younger than Peter, and yet it is a contradiction to suppose that each can be younger than the other. The answer to this is that Peter has not remained in the same inertial system throughout whereas Paul has (if we can neglect the rotation of the Earth and its motion round the Sun). Peter has been in one inertial system on his outward journey and in another on his return journey. He has needed forces to accelerate him and decelerate him, and these forces shift him from one inertial system to another. In figure 6, $OS = OC$ and $SA = DA$ and those who see paradox forget about the interval $CD$. In the figure *three* sets of inertial axes are shown, namely $(OX, OT)$, $(SX', ST')$ and $(SX'', ST'')$. Paul is in one of them throughout, but Peter is in two different ones. It is thus illegitimate, within the assumptions of special relativity, to consider Peter as at rest, since this must be glossed as 'at rest within a single inertial system throughout'. So the supposed contradiction does not arise. This is made very clear by figure 6 itself, where three different inertial sets of axes are shown.

In the light of Einstein's later general theory of relativity, the special theory must be seen as an idealization, approximately true in cases where the concentration of matter and energy is not too great. Einstein's later general theory explains gravitation by postulating a space-time of variable curvature, not the 'flat' space-time of Minkowski. Gravitation is explained geometrically, not causally. The elliptical path of a planet round the Sun can be seen four-dimensionally as a helical world line in Minkowski space, but in Einstein's space-time of variable curvature the world line is not helically curved but lies along a geodesic, which is a generalization of the Euclidean notion of a straight line. In the geometries familiar to most people, a geodesic is the line along which we have the shortest distance between two points. Thus in Euclidean geometry a straight line is a geodesic. On the surface of a sphere, a great circle is a geodesic. That is why aeroplanes from London to Vancouver fly north over Greenland on the way. But because of the minus signs in the definition of space-time geometry, a geodesic can be the *longest* distance between two points. Because of the minus signs like those referred to on p. 27 a geodesic along which a material body, with no forces on it other than gravitation, is hypothesized to lie is actually a maximal, not a minimal distance. In special relativity, too, we have geodesics that are maximal in this way. Thus Paul's world line in figure 6 is a geodesic and *OA* is greater than *OSA* (not less than, as it would be if the figure depicted a Euclidean space). The part *OSA* of Peter's world line is not a geodesic, though its segments *OS* and *SA* are. In making *OS* and *SA* straight I have assumed that we can neglect the gravitational forces on Peter's space ship due to our Sun and the star *S*.

It should be remarked that 'curvature' does not need a higher dimension for its definition. Ordinarily we might say that the surface of a sphere is curved because this curvature can be defined within Euclidean three-dimensional space. Nevertheless, creatures confined to the two-dimensional surface of the sphere could define its curvature intrinsically. If they measure the angles of a triangle on the two-dimensional surface (looking at it three-dimensionally the three sides of the triangle will be great circles on the sphere) they will find that the sum of the angles of the triangle will be greater than two right angles, not equal to it as in 'flat' space. Analogously we can define the curvature of four-dimensional

space-time without reference to a five-dimensional embedding
space.

There may, however, be more respectable reasons why we
should believe that we exist in a space of more than four
dimensions. These reasons arise out of recent attempts to
provide a unified theory of the four forces that are believed to
be the fundamental forces in nature. These are, respectively,
(1) the gravitational force, (2) the electromagnetic force,
(3) the weak interaction, (4) the strong interaction. (The weak
and strong interactions are very short-range forces and it is
the strong interaction that holds an atomic nucleus together.)
The idea is roughly that each point of four-dimensional
space-time has a seven-dimensional space attached to it.
These seven-dimensional spaces are extremely minute, though
unbounded, much as the surface of a sphere is finite but
unbounded. So looked at macroscopically space-time has our
familiar four dimensions but it is (on these speculations)
supposed to have a foamy structure that makes it have eleven
dimensions in the small.

### ABSOLUTE V. RELATIONAL THEORIES OF SPACE-TIME

These considerations are relevant to the controversy about
whether space-time can be analysed in terms of relations
between material objects or whether it is 'absolute', i.e. exists
independently of the material objects within it. (I have said
'material object' here rather than 'physical object', because if
physics does imply the existence of absolute space-time, then
absolute space-time itself should count as a physical object.)
Special relativity showed that space and time taken separately
do not exist, but this does not settle the question of whether
we should hold an absolute theory of *space-time*. It has
commonly been asserted that the theory of relativity favours a
relational theory, but I suspect that in large part this has been
due to a bad pun, a confusion between 'relativity' and
'relationality'. *Prima facie* the *general* theory of relativity

seems positively to favour an absolute theory, since according to this theory it is the variable curvature of space-time that explains gravitation. (The more speculative eleven-dimensional space mentioned in the previous paragraph also suggests very strongly that this elaboration of the theory of space-time represents something independently real.) The question is still controversial, since it is still (so far as I know) an open question whether all the properties of the space-time of general relativity can be explained in terms of the distribution of matter. This is the issue of 'Mach's Principle'. Ernst Mach held that the notion of an inertial system was relative to that of the general distribution of matter in the universe.

Thus consider Isaac Newton's example of the bucket. A bucket is suspended by means of a rope, one end of which is tied to the top of its handle. The surface of the water in the bucket is flat. Now the bucket is slowly rotated many times about a vertical axis so that the rope is twisted tightly. When the bucket is let go the rope will untwist and the bucket will rotate faster and faster until the rope is untwisted again. At first the surface of the water will continue to be flat, but due to viscosity after a bit the water will come to rotate as fast as the bucket itself. As this happens the surface of the water will become concave with the water rising up the sides of the bucket. Later the bucket will stop rotating as the rope gets twisted up again, but for a time the water inside will continue rotating and the surface will remain concave, and will then become flat again as the rotation slows down. Clearly the phenomenon is not due to rotation with respect to the sides of the bucket. Newton thought that it showed that the water is in rotation relative to absolute space. Mach thought otherwise, that it was relative to the fixed stars, which as a whole, therefore, influenced the hollowing out of the surface of the water. (If he had lived these days, he would probably instead of 'fixed stars' have said 'the galaxies'.) He thus enunciated his principle which made inertia depend on the distribution of matter in the universe. My own view is that we need to postulate absolute space-time. The concept of space-time does seem to play a genuinely explanatory role and we should believe in its real existence for much the same reason as we believe in any of the other 'theoretical entities' of physics.

THE ALLEGED 'TRANSITORY' ASPECT OF TIME

I wish now to consider something that has led many philosophers to think that the space-time picture of the world leaves something out. They complain that this picture is 'static' and that it leaves out 'the transitory aspect of time', to use C. D. Broad's expression. Or in other words it is supposed to leave out the idea that time flows, or alternatively the idea that our consciousness advances through time, ever further (until consciousness itself ceases to exist) into the future. I hold that this supposed flow or advance is an illusion. There is something very odd about the concept of a transitory aspect of time. As has very commonly been asked, if time flows how fast does it flow? Does it flow at one second per second? Alternatively does my consciousness advance (up the world line of my body) at one second per second? Do these questions even make sense? Does my ruler advance through space at one centimetre per centimetre? Does the flow or advance of time occur with respect to a hyper-time? Does this hyper-time have flow or advance? Is this in respect to a hyper-hyper-time, and so on? If the hyper-time does not need to have a transitory aspect time itself does not need to have one either. Surely we must reject the transitory aspect of time as some sort of conceptual illusion.

I remarked earlier in this chapter that motion is represented in the Minkowski picture as a matter of relative inclination of world lines. A totally static world would be one in which all world lines of particles were parallel. Clearly the Minkowski world is not like this, and the common assertion that the four-dimensional world would be 'static' makes no sense. Similarly some advocates of the notion of time flow or transitoriness speak of their picture as 'dynamic'. I do not know what they mean by this: they do not mean that all world lines are parallel! The inability of the Minkowski picture to represent flow or advance through time should be seen not as a weakness but as a strength. It is the inability to say something senseless. However, it is easier to convince oneself that the transitory aspect of time is a sort of conceptual illusion than it is to explain the occurrence of the illusion, though I shall make a tentative suggestion about this shortly.

The confusion about flow or passage is enshrined in the etymology of the English word 'past', which is a variant of 'passed'. The idea is that past events are those which have passed by us, flowing from the future into the past, or alternatively, they are events which consciousness has already passed in its supposed advance into the future. We may then say that an event was future, became present and is now past. Trouble then arises if we are led by this to think of pastness, presentness and futurity as properties with respect to which events change. To elucidate this matter I need to explain something about indexical words. Indexical words are words whose reference depends in a rule governed way on who utters them and on their time of utterance. So consequently does the matter of whether the utterance asserts something true or false. Thus if Joe says 'I am tired' at time $t$ then this is true if and only if Joe is (tenseless) tired at time $t$. 'This utterance' said by Joe at $t$ refers to the utterance said by Joe at $t$, i.e. to itself. I think that all indexicals could be paraphrased by means of experiences containing only a single indexical, namely 'this utterance'. Thus 'here' could be paraphrased as 'near the place of this utterance', 'I' could be paraphrased by 'the maker of this utterance', 'you' could be replaced by 'the addressee of this utterance', and so on.

'Past', 'present', 'now', 'future' and the tenses of verbs are indexicals (though tenses have other functions too, which for present purposes we can ignore). Thus to talk of a past event is to talk of something earlier than one's utterance, to talk of a future event is to talk of an event later than one's utterance, to utter 'now' is to refer to an event simultaneous with one's utterance. If one says 'Joe came at $t$' one utters a truth if and only if Joe *comes* earlier than $t$, where I indicate that a verb is to be read as tenseless by putting it in italics. 'Joe will come' uttered at time $t$ asserts a truth if and only if Joe *comes* later than $t$. If Jim utters a sentence 'Joe had come at breakfast time' at time $t$ he utters a truth if Joe *comes* earlier than breakfast time and breakfast time *is* earlier that $t$. 'Joe will have come at breakfast time' asserts a truth if uttered by Joe at $t$ if and only if breakfast time *is* later than $t$ and Joe *comes* earlier than breakfast time. And so on.

Of course Joe might not speak a sentence but write it on a blackboard or in the manuscript of a book. Here the time of utterance should be taken as the initial writing on the blackboard (even though the sentence remains there all through a lecture), or as the initial writing of the manuscript, even though the manuscript is preserved. Similarly in the case of a printed book the utterance is not at the time of the printing but at the time of writing the manuscript.

The above remarks indicate that though we cannot translate a sentence containing indexicals into one not containing indexicals, we can give the rules for its use by means of a non-indexical sentence *about* the original sentence. For example, 'There will be a rabbit here' said by person $P$ at time $t$ *is* true if and only if there *is* a rabbit near $P$ at time $t'$ and $t'$ *is* later than $t$.

We can now see what is wrong with the thought that there really is a change in events from being future through being present to being past. Someone who thinks this is thinking of pastness, presentness and futurity as properties of events much as being red, yellow or green is a property of a signal light. To think this is to forget the indexicality of the words 'past', 'present' and 'future' and their cognates. Indeed it is not even clear what such a sentence as 'Joe's visit to the dentist is future, will be present and then past' could mean. All I can suggest is the following lame statement: if one were to say now that Joe's visit to the dentist is future one would say something true, that if at a certain later time one were to say that Joe's visit to the dentist is present one would once more say something true, and that if at some still later time one were to say that Joe's visit to the dentist is past one would yet again say something true. Once the indexicality is brought out into the open the feeling that there is a real change in events in respect of pastness, presentness and futurity ought to disappear.

Many feminists object to such words as 'chairman' and 'poetess' because they irrelevantly bring in gender. (Statement of gender, they presumably agree, could be made by means of a separate phrase or sentence on occasions on which it is relevant.) Similarly I think that metaphysicians ought to object to tenses, because reference to time relations should not be irrelevantly mixed up with the other functions of verbs. This is not to deny that indexical expressions may be useful in practical life. Suppose that 'The meeting will soon begin' (or less idiomatically, 'The meeting *begins* ten minutes after now') is said to Joe who has left his watch at home. It clearly has a practical informative function, e.g. said to Joe who has left his watch at home, and when no clock is within the range of Joe's vision, which 'The meeting *begins* at 2 p.m.' could not possibly have.

Since the notion of 'present' or 'now' depends on that of simultaneity, it would seem that even this practical use of tenses might be vitiated by the relativity of simultaneity. Of course this would show up only if persons wished to communicate with one another if they were in relative motion at velocities comparable to that of light. If fast space ships were to make this a practical consideration a convention could be adopted according to which 'now' referred to events that were simultaneous in the inertial system in which the utterer was at rest. This would of course be awkward for the addressee who would need to make quick computations about relative velocities in order fully to understand the message.

The fact that normally we are concerned with communication between persons who move slowly (as compared with the velocity of light) relative to one another is a special case of a fact to which the Cambridge philosopher Jeremy Butterfield has recently drawn attention. He has pointed out that the time lag in observational reaction time and oral communication time is usually smaller than the times between which objects change their salient observable properties. Obviously there is a good evolutionary explanation of many cases of why this is so: if reaction time had been longer than the time a rock took to roll down a mountain this would not have been conducive to survival. (Obviously selection can work the other way too: the striking of a snake might be salient to our shocked vision but would be too fast for our ability to react in time. But by and large Butterfield's remark holds good.) There is also the explanation that many physical processes are far too fast for an electrochemical nervous system that has developed in the way ours has ever to evolve to being a much faster one. Therefore many properties that might have been salient are just unobservable by us. Butterfield has argued that this fact (that the speed at which physical things observably change with respect to their observable properties is usually slow in relation to the reaction time and oral communication time of agents) explains the fact that we indicate temporal position by tenses, whereas we do not have tenses to indicate spatial position. He says that, because of the relative rapidity of oral communication, people can share a 'now', while if they are some way apart, they do not share a 'here'.

Though I am sure that our advance through time, or the flow of time past us (as if bearing us down a river to the great waterfall which is our death) is an illusion, I am not sure how to explain how the illusion comes about. It is tempting to think that the illusion comes from misunderstanding the indexicals 'past', 'present' and 'future', and thinking of change in respect of futurity as analogous to the change of a signal light from red to green. The trouble is that, as I hinted a few pages back, the etymology of the word 'past' suggests that such words were antecedently infested with 'the myth of passage', to use D. C. Williams's nice expression. Moreover, it does seem plausible that persons who shared a language without tenses or words such as 'past', 'present', 'future' and 'now' would still feel as though they were being borne down the river of time. I am *inclined* to conjecture that it is the flow of information through our short-term memory that gets confused with a flow of time itself. (The answer does not seem likely to lie in an increase in our long-term memory. It seems plausible that a very old man who was losing long-term memories faster than he was gaining them would still have the feeling that time was flowing in the same direction as that in which in his youth he had felt that it flowed.)

### TRACES, MEMORIES AND DIRECTION IN TIME

The phenomenon of memory is a special case of the more general phenomenon of a *trace*. Why are memories, tape recordings, footprints in the sand, fossils, photographs, and so on traces of past events, never of future ones? Some philosophers might wrongly be tempted to dismiss this as a silly question, like the question why there are no female uncles.

It is part of the meaning of the word 'trace', they might say, that traces are of earlier events. This would be a shallow and unhelpful reply to what I believe is a profound question. It may be part of what we mean by 'uncle' that uncles are male, but there is an obvious female analogue of an uncle, namely an aunt. If we conceded that it was part of the meaning of 'trace' that traces are of earlier events, we could still ask why there is no future analogue of a trace, just as there is a female analogue of an uncle. There is of course *prediction* of future events but this is the analogue not of memory of past events but of retrodiction. In both prediction and retrodiction we make an explicit deduction from certain laws of nature together with statements of boundary conditions at a particular time over a chunk of space within which the system under consideration is relatively isolated.

The general asymmetry with respect to traces suggests that the universe is asymmetrical in the time direction in a way in which it is not asymmetrical with respect to space directions. This asymmetry is connected with an important statistical feature of the universe, which is expressed by the second law of thermodynamics. This says that a closed system will evolve from a more orderly to more disordered state. This can be illustrated by the example of the molecules of air in a room. Suppose that there is an equal chance of a given molecule being in any cubic centimetre of space within the room. The most probable state will be the normal one in which the density of air is (near enough) constant from one part of it to another. A very highly ordered (very improbable) state would be one in which the molecules were in one half of the room with a vacuum in the other half. The improbability is so great that we would not expect it to occur by chance even if the room and its air could exist for a time equal to the whole previous history (since the big bang) of the universe. We must nevertheless regard the second law of thermodynamics as statistical only, and we do come across small observable statistical fluctuations in the other direction, as in the case of the Brownian motion in which pollen particles are moved about through inequalities in the way in which molecules happen to strike different sides of the particles.

Traces can be explained as what H. Reichenbach called 'branch systems'. These are certain relatively isolated systems in which disorder is less than in the surroundings. Thus consider a volume of sand on a beach, say six inches deep, and a few yards in diameter, and with a footprint in its centre. The footprint is a trace of an interaction of a walker with the beach. The sand has been crushed into a more improbable and more ordered state. Where before there had been a certain uniform density of molecules there is now just empty air above and adjacent to a volume in which the sand is crushed so that the density of molecules of the sand is greater than it was before. The six inch deep volume of sand (later of air and sand) is now in what was antecedently an improbable (more ordered) state. Reichenbach held that traces of all sorts, such as recordings on a magnetic tape or the brain traces that constitute memory, can be elucidated as branch systems, as in the case of the footprint. Some details of Reichenbach's treatment have been questioned, but the general idea has been developed by Adolf Grünbaum and others. It would appear, then, that the fact that we remember the past and not the future has an explanation in terms of statistical mechanics. So does the fact that milk and coffee mix together to make a brownish white liquid, whereas we never see the milk and coffee separate themselves out from the brownish white. It is not contrary to the fundamental laws of nature that the molecules in the milky coffee should by chance separate out, the milky ones going upwards and the coffee molecules all going downwards. It is just that it is more than astronomically unlikely.

Let us reflect more on the temporal asymmetry of the universe (or at the least of our cosmic region of it). We never observe spontaneous unmixing of milk and coffee. We never observe a brick lying on the lawn being pushed up to fly into the air on account of a coincidental upwards movement of molecules in the soil. Yet it is surely merely the reverse of a process that we observe, a brick falling on to a lawn and having its kinetic energy of motion being dissipated in unco-ordinated motions of the molecules of the soil of the lawn. A reverse process with the brick lying on the lawn and then suddenly rising into the air, because all the molecules in the lawn had by chance had the reverse motion to those they had acquired when the brick had landed on it before, is physically possible. It is of course improbable in the extreme because of the chance co-ordination of the molecules in the lawn that would be needed. Actually some of the energy of the brick when it fell on to the lawn would have dissipated as radiant heat, which is electromagnetic energy, and which is made up of photons. To have the reverse process we would need to have photons coming in from the outside and being absorbed by the atoms of the lawn. This illustrates another source of asymmetry, that we never observe spherical waves of light or other electromagnetic radiation (to speak classically) coming into a sink, whereas it is a familiar fact that such spherical waves go out from a source. This is a statistical matter too: it is not against the laws of nature that spherical waves should come into a sink: merely improbable in the extreme.

Suppose that we were to film bricks falling on to lawns, milk mixing with coffee, and so on, and that we were to play this film backwards. What we would see would be as much in accordance with the laws of mechanics and electrodynamics (bizarre though it would look to us) as when it was played forwards. It would be improbable in the extreme that we should ever come across such occurrences, so improbable that if we did seem to we would not be rational to believe our own eyes. (Rather we should consult a psychiatrist, or something like that.) It seems to be a fact, explicable perhaps by cosmological thermodynamics, that all or nearly all branch systems point the same way in time. Suppose, however, that there were some remote part of the universe where all branch systems and all or nearly all thermodynamic processes pointed in the reverse direction, then memories would be reversed too, and occurrences in that part of the universe would not look at all bizarre to inhabitants of it. If like us they were prone to the illusion that time flows they would have the illusion that it flows in the opposite direction to that in which we tend to think that it flows.

There is of course a direction away from the big bang, from which the universe has expanded. This gives a direction in which time-like world lines could be said to have a preferred direction. This symmetry might be restored if the big bang had been preceded by a big squeeze. Whether the universe will continue to expand for ever or will fall back to a big squeeze under the gravitational energy and matter in it is a conjectural matter. Present opinion seems to be that the expansion is delicately balanced with the gravitational force of contraction, and the answer to the question of whether or not the expansion will go on for ever depends on changing estimates of the density of matter and energy in the universe at large.

I have noted three cosmic asymmetries: (1) the thermo-dynamic or statistical asymmetries epitomized by branch systems; (2) the asymmetry of waves expanding from a source, as opposed to contracting to a sink; (3) the expansion of the universe. It is an interesting question, which has concerned some theoretical physicists and cosmologists, whether these three asymmetries may be reduced to a single one.

These asymmetries would exist even though the laws of nature were time-symmetric. By and large the laws are time-symmetric but not quite. Recondite experiments have turned up violations of time symmetry. Let us consider three symmetries: (1) charge symmetry; (2) parity symmetry; and (3) time symmetry. Charge symmetry implies that if in the fundamental laws of nature you replaced 'electron' by 'positron' and vice versa, 'proton' by 'anti-proton' and vice versa, and so on for all particles with positive or negative electric charge, you would still have the same laws. Parity implies that if the universe were reflected as if in a mirror it would still obey the fundamental laws of nature; time sym-metry implies that the laws of nature would not be altered under time reversal, i.e. if everywhere you replaced '$t$' by '$-t$'. It was discovered in 1957 by C. S. Wu and others that the weak interaction, which is responsible for a certain process in which a nucleus of an atom spontaneously ejects an electron or a positron, violates parity. It was conjectured that nevertheless there is a $CP$ invariance, i.e. invariance if you both reverse charge and reverse parity. An experiment by J. H. Christensen and others (1964) showed that $CP$ symmetry was violated too. It is therefore now believed that $T$ symmetry is violated, but that there is $CPT$ symmetry, i.e. things go on as before if you reverse charge, reflect as in a mirror and reverse time.

These violations of time symmetry do not seem important in ordinary contexts. For most purposes we can regard the laws of nature as time-symmetrical. I think it unlikely that the illusion of time asymmetry that we experience when we think that time flows one way is related to the difference between $T$ symmetry and $CPT$ symmetry. It seems that the sort of explanation of memory traces and so on which is based on Reichenbach's theory of branch systems, in the context of statistical mechanics, is on the right track and that it would work just as well if the laws of nature were completely time-symmetric, as indeed to a high degree they actually are. In any case we do not need any notion of time flow in order to explain the temporal asymmetry of the universe, in particular the asymmetry with respect to traces. Even if the notion of time flow made sense, explanations by reference to it would be too facile.

### ATTITUDES TO PAST AND FUTURE

A. N. Prior, who was a friend of tense and time flow, has stressed the feeling of 'Thank goodness that's over'. Now certainly we do have attitudes to the future different from those we have to the past. Prior says that when we thank goodness that our visit to the dentist is past we are not thanking goodness that our visit to the dentist is earlier than our present utterance. He asks why we should thank goodness for *that*. A de-tenser such as myself can reply that due to the asymmetry of the universe with respect to memory traces and the like we plan for the future, not the past. Planning is an information flow process and in view of the asymmetry about traces information flows from earlier to later. Thus we plan for the future and steel ourselves against future pain. Since planning is of use for survival, our different attitudes to past and future have been built into our species by natural selection. We may say 'Thank goodness that's over' because there is now no need to make plans or worry any more. Of course a trait that has been selected because it is useful for survival need not be useful in all ways or circumstances. A prisoner who knows that he will be executed next day will feel fear and apprehension and will be far more unhappy in consequence. Fear has a general usefulness, since it promotes avoiding action, for example when a person is confronted by a poisonous snake, but that does not mean that it is useful when avoiding action is impossible. Does the possibility of planning the future imply that the future is indeterminate? On the space-time view the future must of course be determinate. Some readers may sense a difficulty here. I shall try to deal with this in chapter 6.

## ETERNAL OBJECTS

Are there any things in the world that are not in space-time? Perhaps there is a God who is eternal, outside space-time. Perhaps we have to recognize the existence of such things as numbers and sets of numbers, and perhaps such things as properties. These will not be in space-time. We must not close off the issue by saying that to exist means to be in space and time, or in space-time. '$\phi$ exists' just means 'There *is* a $\phi$'. (I have made the 'exists' and 'is' tenseless. Indeed in modern classical logic the 'existential quantifier', meaning 'there is a', is always to be read tenselessly.) Now a $\phi$ may exist in space-time just as a rose may exist botanically or a tiger zoologically. To be spatio-temporal is no more part of what it is to exist than is to be a plant or an animal. Indeed if the absolute (as opposed to the relational) theory of space-time is correct, then space-time points exist, and yet it is in only a trivial sense that they could be said to be *in* space-time. Numbers, if they exist, do not exist in space-time.

Do numbers, sets of numbers, sets of sets of these, and so on really exist? If they do, they are eternal objects, i.e. non-spatiotemporal. W. V. Quine calls them 'Platonic'. Such a

Platonic philosophy of mathematics could be avoided if in some way talk of numbers and so on could be elucidated as talk about physical entities. Then numbers and sets might disappear from our ontology, talk ostensibly about them being paraphrased in terms that do not carry this commitment. Compare ostensible reference to a strange entity 'the average plumber'. This does not worry us because we can translate 'The average plumber weighs 170 lb' (for example) as 'The total weight in lbs of all the plumbers divided by the number of plumbers is 170.' Perhaps the most interesting attempt to avoid Platonism in mathematics in this sort of way has been due to Hartry Field, but has not met with general acceptance. At present I would like to keep an open mind on the matter, but as matters stand, I am inclined towards Platonism about mathematical entities. Quine's argument seems convincing. He points out that a physical theory apparently contains reference to mathematical objects inextricably mixed up with reference to spatio-temporal objects. The predictive success of the theory gives us good reason to believe in the existence of the Platonic objects no less than in the electrons, protons, etc., postulated in the theory. The argument is an argument to the best explanation: the best explanation of the predictive success of a theory that ostensibly mentions Platonic objects may well be the simple one that there really are Platonic objects.

Another type of philosopher may propose another sort of entities that do not exist in space-time, namely minds. Philosophers who deny that minds are spatial normally hold that they are in time. So they are not eternal objects in the way that numbers perhaps are. Confronted by special relativity and the question 'Which time?' they may identify a person's time dimension with the world line of his or her body, or perhaps brain, except that this world line would be a proper geometrical line, whereas a body or brain defines a world line which is really a very thin tube through space-time. However, I shall argue in chapters 4 and 5 for the view that roughly speaking the mind is identical with the brain, and if I am correct in this there is no reason to believe in minds as temporal but non-spatial entities.

Some physicists have been tempted into a philosophical theory called 'phenomenalism' according to which matter is no more than 'a permanent possibility of sensation'. According to this theory talking about physical objects, whether electrons or rock melons, is just a way of talking about our sense experiences. I shall look briefly at this theory in chapter 3, but the main objections will come in chapter 5.

SUGGESTIONS FOR FURTHER READING AND
BIBLIOGRAPHICAL REFERENCES

For further of my views on the concerns of this chapter see my papers 'Space-Time and Individuals', in Richard Rudner and Israel Scheffler (eds), *Logic and Art: essays in honor of Nelson Goodman* (New York: Macmillan, 1972), and 'Time and Becoming', in Peter van Inwagen (ed.), *Time and Cause* (Dordrecht: Reidel, 1980), which were reprinted in J. J. C. Smart, *Essays Metaphysical and Moral* (Oxford: Basil Blackwell, 1987). Minkowski's 1908 paper and Einstein's 1905 one will be found in H. A. Lorentz, A. Einstein, H. Minkowski and H. Weyl, *The Principle of Relativity*, translated by W. Perrett and G. B. Jeffery (New York: Dover, 1923). A good philosophy of space-time in a nutshell may be found in the entry 'Space-Time' in W. V. Quine, *Quiddities: an intermittently philosophical dictionary* (Cambridge, Mass.: Harvard University Press, 1987). For a popular account of space and time in physics, see P. C. W. Davies, *Space and Time in the Modern Universe* (Cambridge: Cambridge University Press, 1977). On time asymmetry see Paul Horwich, *Time Asymmetries* (Boston, Mass.: MIT Press, 1987), and P. C. W. Davies, *The Physics of Time Asymmetry*, 2nd edn (Berkeley: University of California Press, 1985). The latter book is fairly technical but should be readable by anyone with first year university mathematics. Also fairly difficult is A. Grünbaum, *Philosophical Problems of Space and Time*, 2nd edn (Dordrecht: Reidel, 1973). Graham Nerlich, *The Shape of Space* (Cambridge: Cambridge University Press, 1976) defends absolute space-time, as does Ian Hinckfuss, *The Existence of Space and Time* (Oxford:

Clarendon Press, 1975). A. S. Eddington, *Space, Time and Gravitation* (Cambridge: Cambridge University Press, 1920) is a classic popularization of the special and general theories of relativity, and it contains some interesting but questionable philosophy. For an account of recent speculations about eleven-dimensional space-time see P. C. W. Davies, *Superforce: the search for a grand unified theory of nature* (London: Heinemann, 1984), especially chapter 10. On the semantics of indexicals, see Donald Davidson, *Inquiries into Truth and Interpretation* (Oxford: Clarendon Press, 1984), p. 34.

Other references are as follows: Ernst Mach, *The Science of Mechanics: a critical and historical account of its development*, translated by J. McCormack, 6th edn (La Salle, Ill.: Open Court, 1960), chapter 6, section 6; D. H. Mellor, *Real Time* (Cambridge: Cambridge University Press, 1981); C. D. Broad, *Examination of McTaggart's Philosophy*, vol. 2, part 1 (Cambridge: Cambridge University Press, 1938), chapter 35; D. C. Williams, 'The Myth of Passage', *Journal of Philosophy*, *48* (1951) 457–72, reprinted in D. C. Williams, *Principles of Empirical Realism* (Springfield, Ill.: Charles C. Thomas, 1966); H. Reichenbach, *The Direction of Time* (Berkeley: University of California Press, 1956); P. T. Geach, 'Some Problems about Time', in P. F. Strawson (ed.), *Studies in the Philosophy of Thought and Action* (Oxford: Clarendon Press, 1968); A. N. Prior, 'Thank Goodness That's Over', *Philosophy*, *34* (1959), 12–17, reprinted in A. N. Prior, *Papers on Logic and Ethics* (London: Duckworth, 1976); W. V. Quine, *From a Logical Point of View*, 2nd edn revised (New York: Harper & Row, 1961), chapter 1; Hartry Field, *Science without Numbers* (Oxford: Basil Blackwell, 1980). The papers by Einstein, Minkowski and Williams mentioned above, as well as extracts from the books by Mach, Broad and Eddington, have been reprinted in J. J. C. Smart (ed.), *Problems of Space and Time* (New York: Macmillan, 1964). Jeremy Butterfield's idea, mentioned on p. 38 above, is worked out in his paper 'Seeing the Present', *Mind*, *93* (1984), 161–76.

# 3

# Physics and Reality

## PHYSICS AND COMMON SENSE

In his popular book *The Nature of the Physical World* Sir Arthur Eddington propounded a memorable paradox. He spoke of the table on which he was writing, and rather playfully distinguished two tables: the common sense table and the table as known to science. The common sense table is brown, solid and inert, while the scientific table is made up of particles such as electrons and protons, of which colour cannot be meaningfully predicated, and in rapid motion and separated by empty space, so that their combined bulk amounts to a tiny proportion of the bulk of the table itself. Which is the real table, or are both real?

Some philosophers and scientists plump for the common sense table. They want to say that physics is just a dodge for predicting occurrences among those things that we can see or feel with our ordinary senses. Some, such as Ernst Mach, even went further and said that talk of common sense objects (e.g. tables) is itself just a dodge for predicting regularities among our sense experiences. That is, they combine scepticism about Eddington's scientific table with a scepticism about ordinary commonsense objects, or else, what does not seem to me to be ontologically very different, they claim that statements about common sense objects can at least approximately be translated into sentences about sense experiences.

This is the philosophical doctrine called 'phenomenalism' and in essence it goes back to the great eighteenth-century philosopher Bishop Berkeley. Consideration of phenomenalism will have to wait until chapter 5, when I shall be concerned with matters to do with perception and the nature of mind. Let us provisionally take it that the common sense table is real and that talk of it cannot be reduced to talk of sense experiences.

Other philosophers, of whom I am one, would accept the reality of both the common sense table and the scientific table: the scientific table just is the common sense table. What is different is our mode of describing it, much as when one and the same person might be described either as the professor of anatomy or as the dean of the medical faculty. The discussion of colour will also have to wait until chapter 5, but let me anticipate by saying that the colours of objects such as tables are (rather idiosyncratic) *physical* states of their surfaces. They are macroscopic, in that one cannot ascribe colours to individual particles or even atoms or molecules. This does not prevent colours from being physical. Physics is quite familiar with macroscopic properties that cannot be possessed by individual atoms or molecules. A macroscopic object can be crystalline, i.e. its constituent atoms can be arranged in a regular lattice, but the individual atoms obviously cannot be a regular lattice of atoms. Similarly, if we say that the table is solid, meaning thereby that a book placed on it will not fall through the table (as it would fall through a swarm of flies), we have something compatible with the scientific story. As Eddington pointed out in his discussion of 'the two tables', the particles in the table, in their violent motion, will keep bumping into the particles in the book above it, and the book will be supported as satisfactorily as if it and the table and book were continuous substances whose intrinsic nature was to occupy space to the exclusion of other substances. One might question, as Susan Stebbing did in her book *Philosophy and the Physicists*, whether the common sense notion of solidity does imply this metaphysics of continuous substances, and whether the scientific account of the solidity of macroscopic objects is incompatible with the common sense notion of it.

When Eddington said that the table was not solid he meant that it consisted of physical particles whose combined volume (in so far as one can speak intelligibly of the volumes of elementary particles) is minute compared with the volume of the table itself. In this sense, of course, the table is not solid. This has no bearing on the question of whether we speak falsely when we contrast the solidity of the table with that of a swarm of flies, which certainly will not support books or do as a writing desk. Thus a good deal of reconciliation is possible between theoretical physics and common sense. I do not mean that a *complete* reconciliation is possible. If 'solid' is taken to mean that there is no empty space between the particles of which the table is composed, and if common sense is taken to assert this, then the table is not solid and common sense is at fault. If common sense is what the man in the pub believes, a lot depends on what pub it is and on the literacy of its clientele. It is unclear therefore just what has to be reconciled with what. In chapter 6 I shall consider a similar near reconciliation between determinism (or an approximation to it) and our ordinary concept of free will, and once more there will be the problem of how much to build into the notion of 'our ordinary concept'.

### REALITY AND TRUTH

What about those philosophers and scientists who, as I remarked near the beginning of this chapter, plump exclusively for the reality of the common sense table, that is, who think of talk about electrons, neutrinos, curved space-time and so on as merely a useful dodge for predicting what can be observed at the macroscopic level in the laboratory, or with instruments or by means of telescopes? Their espousal of such a philosophy was partly due to an extreme of empiricist thought, which though a healthy reaction to *a priori*

metaphysics, like most reactions went too far. Even Newton
said that he did not make hypotheses, and yet of course he in
fact made wonderful and beautiful hypotheses. Partly it has in
recent times come from reflection on the apparently paradoxical nature of quantum mechanics. In the case of some
scientists it also comes from unnecessary suspicion of
perfectly good English words like 'true' and 'real'. These are
sometimes put by scientists in shudder quotation marks, and
are thought of as horrid mushy words in contrast to sensible
words such as 'geodesic' or 'neutrino' that are used by
scientists.

As an example of this last tendency consider the following
quotations from an important and very interesting paper by
Brandon Carter, a cosmologist who will be mentioned again
in chapter 7. Carter says that there is a 'widespread
misconception among philosophers to the effect that science
is concerned with "reality".' (Carter allows that it is
concerned with 'realism' but the distinction is obscure to me.)
He also rejects the idea that 'theories should precisely
represent universal "truth".' In practice, he says, 'science is
not concerned with under-lying truth, but more modestly
(and by its own criteria, more successfully) with providing
the most simple, coherent and comprehensive possible
description of *appearance*.' Note the shudder quotation
marks. Shudder quotation marks round 'truth' look odd to
those familiar with Alfred Tarski's precise definition of truth
for formalized languages, or even to those who simply note
the unmysteriousness of 'snow is white' being true if and only
if snow is white. Similarly the shudder quotation marks
round 'real' look odd to those of us who believe that to say
'unicorns are real' is just to say that there are unicorns.
Admittedly we have to look suspiciously on 'There are unicorns
in mythology', but here the philosophically misleading
expression is 'in mythology'. (There are no unicorns, but
some myths assert that there are.) It is true that scientists
often purport to refer to 'ideal objects', such as Newtonian
mass points, but I regard this as a pretence use of the ordinary

'there are', so that if they say 'there really are no mass points' they are acknowledging that this is a pretence use and that talk of Newtonian mass points is at best approximately true for the purposes of certain contexts. To say 'there really are electrons' is just to say 'there are electrons' with a warning not to take this with a pinch of salt.

### REALISM AND ANTI-REALISM

Those scientists who do not have unnecessary qualms about 'true' and 'real' and who are not seduced by extreme empiricist or 'positivist' philosophy will mostly assume that in their theories they are talking about real things and are not merely using a dodge for making predictions about observations in the laboratory or in the observatory. Consider, for example, theories about what happened in the first few moments after the 'big bang' from which the universe is supposed to have originated. I conjecture that most cosmologists, perhaps even Carter most of the time, think of this as real history, no less than conjectures about dinosaurs, or even about the battle of Waterloo. Now can such an implicit attitude be justified philosophically?

We shall be concerned with arguments for the reality of what we may call the 'theoretical entities' of science. The terminology is slightly misleading because one and the same thing may be a theoretical entity in one context and an observational entity in another context. Thus there is a sense in which a murder may be a theoretical entity for Sherlock Holmes but an object of perception and memory for the criminal. We know about electrons, neutrinos, curved space-time and so on more in the way that Sherlock Holmes knows about the murder than in the way that the criminal does or an eyewitness would. We cannot directly perceive these entities. We know about them from galvanometer readings, spectrometer photographs, bubble chamber tracks, observations of the position of Mercury, and so on. But then we cannot directly perceive dinosaurs though we could have done so if we had lived at an appropriate place and time. Sherlock Holmes was not able to perceive the murder, though he could have done so if he had been appropriately placed. The difference with the so-called 'theoretical entities' of physics is that there are physical reasons why we could not directly perceive them. For example, physicists know about neutrinos because the postulation of them provides a plausible explanation of some fetures of certain bubble chamber tracks. It all fits in with a web of belief (to use a metaphor favoured by W. V. Quine) about electric charges, conservation of momentum and of energy, and various other things. Because of their lack of charge, neutrinos do not leave bubble chamber or cloud chamber tracks, but the neutrino was postulated to balance up the momenta of other particles which did show themselves by such tracks. The reasoning is holistic, and depends on the best way either of preserving the web of belief or of reconstructing it without wholly destroying it as a philosophical sceptic would wish to do. (A thoroughgoing philosophical scepticism never succeeds, because without a web of belief of some sort we would be dead.) I have given the example of the neutrino, because the evidence for its existence is very indirect, but of course the evidence for even those particles that do leave bubble chamber tracks is indirect too, though to a lesser degree.

Now a scientific anti-realist might say that all the evidence shows is that the world is just *as if* there were electrons, neutrinos, etc. The postulation of them, according to the anti-realist, is a sort of fairy story which is not to be believed: it is there just so that we can put some order into our observations and predict fresh observations. My reaction to this is to express incredulity. Is it not implausible that things should be merely 'as if', at least on a holistic scale? Certainly there are isolated analogies that legitimately enable us to talk in terms of 'as if'. We can of course say such a thing as that an inductor and a capacitor in series oscillate electrically just as if the oscillations were mechanical and the inductor was a heavy mass and the capacitor a spring. Certainly there are these isolated analogies that enable us to talk merely of 'as if'. Nevertheless it is most unplausible that the laboratory phenomena taken as a whole, or at any rate over a wide scope are just *as if* there were the theoretical entities. Would not rejection of full-blooded realism about the theoretical entities be as bad as if Sherlock Holmes were to say that the footprint on the rose bed, the blood in the library, the disappearance of the butler, etc., was just *as if* there had been a murder? Admittedly Sherlock Holmes may ultimately come to grip the murderer by the collar, and we cannot do anything like this with electrons, neutrinos or curved space-time. The realist can counter this objection by saying that there are theoretical reasons why we cannot grip the theoretical entities (metaphorically) by the collar, and so can accept one part of the analogy while reasonably rejecting another part of it. Our knowledge of the physics and physiology of perception explains why we cannot perceive individual atoms or electrons.

Suppose that Sherlock Holmes comes to the conclusion that the butler was the murderer. He does so because this is overwhelmingly the simplest hypothesis to explain the facts. Critics of so-called 'circumstantial evidence' are in effect complaining that there could be other hypotheses that would be consistent with the evidence. Obviously the circumstantiality of evidence is a matter of degree – the less plausible the other hypotheses the less the circumstantiality. Even the best evidence (short of direct perception) is circumstantial to some degree. Even if blood were found on the butler's hands, and shown by laboratory tests (not available in Sherlock Holmes's day) to be the victim's blood, and if the butler signed a detailed confession, a fantastic and unplausible but self-consistent hypothesis could be proposed that would be consistent with the butler's innocence. Readers of the Sherlock Holmes stories may remember that Holmes talked of 'deducing' the identity of the criminal. This, however, was loose talk that if taken literally would suggest that Holmes's ability to theorize about logic was greatly inferior to his ability to apply scientific method.

Bas van Fraassen, in his fine book *The Scientific Image*, defended the view that the aim of theoretical science is to give us 'empirically adequate theories'. A theory is empirically adequate provided that its observational consequences are true. The theory itself need not be true. Van Fraassen differs from positivists, who hold that theoretical statements can be translated into purely observational ones (which is a doctrine easily refuted), and instrumentalists, who hold that theoretical statements are strictly meaningless and are merely part of a meaningless algorithm that enables us to get from true observation statements to other true observational statements, and hence to make predictions.

Van Fraassen holds that theories may be meaningful in the sense that they have a model. Let me now pause to explain rather informally the notion as it occurs in modern logic. (I shall also occasionally need the notion of a model in later chapters.) The word 'model' is used in other ways by scientists, as when, for example, they say that the brain makes a 'model' of the external world. In logic, what is said to have a model is a set of sentences. In what follows I shall assume that science can be expressed in classical logic. (Science will need mathematics, which can be reduced to set theory, but set theory can be expressed in classical logic too.) Classical logic is the logic developed by Frege, Whitehead and Russell, and Quine, and is concerned with the words 'not', 'or', 'some', 'all', 'is identical with', and words defined in terms of them. For example, in classical logic 'If $p$ then $q$' is just 'not $p$ or $q$'. This preserves the important thing about 'If . . . then . . .' in ordinary language, which is that from '$p$' and 'If $p$ then $q$' we can deduce '$q$'.

Consider the following sentences: 'Joe loves Mary', 'Mary eats an apple' and 'Joe does not eat an apple.' In the notation of classical logic we would write these as 'loves ( Joe, Mary)', '$(\exists x)$(apple $x$ . Mary eats $x$)', '$\sim(\exists x)$(apple $x$ . Joe eats $x$)'. Read '.' as 'and', and '$\sim$' as 'it is not the case that' and '$\exists x$' as 'there is an $x$ such that'. We make a model as follows. Associate the names 'Joe' and 'Mary' with the natural numbers 3 and 16 respectively, and the predicate 'loves' with the set of pairs of natural numbers such that the first is less than the second, so that 'Joe loves Mary' is true in the model because 3 is less than 16. Associate the predicate 'eats' with the set of natural numbers such that the first is the square of the second. Associate the predicate 'is an apple' with the set of natural numbers $\{4, 5, 6, 7\}$. Thus 'Mary eats an apple' is true in the model because 16 is the square of 4. 'Joe does not eat an apple' is true in the model because 3 is not the square of 4, 5, 6 or 7. (Indeed it is not the square of any natural number, the natural numbers being 0, 1, 2, 3, . . . .) Thus our finite set of sentences has a model in the arithmetic of the natural numbers.

There is a remarkable theorem in classical logic, the Skolem–Löwenheim theorem, which says that any consistent set of sentences (whether a finite or infinite set of sentences) has a model in the natural numbers. Of course a model need not be an arithmetical one. Thus a certain class of sentences about an electric circuit consisting of an inductor and capacitor in series can be modelled in mechanics, where 'is an inductor' is associated with a set of masses and 'is a capacitor' is associated with a set of springs, each mass being connected to one spring. As was remarked a few pages back, a circuit consisting of an inductor (a coil) and a capacitor in series will oscillate just as a weight suspended from a spring will do.

To return now to van Fraassen. Van Fraassen holds that theories are meaningful in the sense that they have models. (So he does not regard them as made up of meaningless marks useful for computation as a pure instrumentalist would do.) The realist will hold that one of the models that a set of true theoretical sentences has is the real world. Van Fraassen is agnostic about this. He is concerned not with the truth of a theory but with empirical adequacy, namely that the set of the theory's observation sentences (which will be a sub-class of sentences in the language of the theory) will have a model in the real world. Van Fraassen agrees of course that the whole theory has some model or other. Indeed the Skolem–Löwenheim theorem ensures this. Where he differs from the realist is in denying that the theory need be true, i.e. that the real world need be one of its models.

Van Fraassen acknowledges that 'observable' is a vague predicate. He counts a look through a telescope at the moons of Jupiter as a clear case of observation because the moons could be (and doubtless one day will be) seen directly with the naked eye. He is much more doubtful about 'observation' of a charged particle by looking at its cloud chamber track, though of course if such a thing is allowed as on the observation side of the theory/observation dichotomy what he says about things on the theory side of the dichotomy still go through. It seems to me that allowing such arbitrariness in the theory/observation dichotomy removes much of the appeal which van Fraassen's sort of anti-realism might be thought to have. Such arbitrariness would seem to imply that 'exists' or 'real' are vague words, and this seems to me nonsense. A thing cannot half-exist.

Let us suppose, then, that we use the word 'observe' so that what we observe is what could be perceived by a person without scientific training. This removes (or at least reduces) the arbitrariness of 'observe', but we get into difficulty in another way. Eddington held that what physics is about is 'pointer readings'. Certainly a person without scientific training could report that a pointer was adjacent to a certain numeral on the dial of an ammeter, even though he did not understand the term 'ampere'. However, there are no laws or tight regularities in the realm of pointer readings. Consider a resistor with an ammeter in series with it and a voltmeter in parallel with it. Suppose that the ammeter has its pointer opposite the numeral '10' when the voltmeter has its pointer opposite to the numeral '20'. Now you put in an extra battery or something and the voltmeter pointer is opposite '20' when the ammeter pointer is opposite '20'. Does this disprove Ohm's law, that current varies as voltage? Of course not: it is more likely that the ammeter or the voltmeter is defective. The ammeter or voltmeter has to be calibrated. This might be by reference to another ammeter or voltmeter. This obviously only postpones the problem. We relate the behaviour of the ammeter to the definition of an ampere of electric current in terms of the force per metre exerted by one of two infinite parallel wires with a certain current in each of the two wires. (Ampère's own definition was in terms of the force exerted on a small magnet by a loop of wire.) It is hard to get rid of theory altogether – reference to a pointer reading obscures the problems.

It might be attempted to get right down to common sense observation, with no reference to theory, so called 'operational definitions'. Investigation of this idea would show that it would suffer from conclusive objections similar to some of those which vitiate the phenomenalist or Berkeleyan theory about ordinary material objects, against which I shall argue in chapter 5.

Moreover, operational definitions can soon lose that status and become empirical or theoretical laws. Theoretically current is flux of electric charge, and this relates to the charge on an individual electron. This theoretical notion is more fundamental, and the definition used by standards laboratories can be seen as secondary. The sentences of physics are a network of the more and the less theoretical, but none can be fully understood without some background of theory. Physics may have begun in common sense, but in developing its common sense beginnings it has become part of our increasingly theoretical web of belief. I shall not press this objection to the theory/observation distinction, because, as we saw, van Fraassen is willing to allow that the distinction is vague and one of degree. However, it may lend a certain unplausibility to van Fraassen's position.

Van Fraassen and I both stress, from opposite points of view, the question of *representation* of the world by our theories. Ian Hacking has stressed *intervention*. It seems to me that representation and intervention are hard to disentangle from one another. Hacking in his book *Representing and Intervening*, p. 23, discussed an experiment by physicists at Stanford with the object of detecting quarks (hypothesized particles) by trying to detect changes of electric charge (on a niobium ball) of one-third the charge, positive or negative, of an electron. The experimenters altered the charge on the ball by 'spraying it with positrons or electrons'. Hacking remarks: 'From that day forth I've been a scientific realist. *So far as I'm concerned, if you can spray them then they are real.*' While I am in agreement with this, I would stress that the concept of reality should not be tied to that of causal intervention, or even to causality in general. Indeed it should not be tied to any property whatever. Descartes produced a fallacious proof of the existence of God (the most perfect being). He asked us to imagine a perfect being without at first considering whether the being exists. He then said that an existent being is more perfect than a non-existent being. So the most perfect being must exist. The trouble with Descartes' argument is his treating 'exists' in 'God exists' as a predicate, whereas the logical form of 'God exists' is rather 'There is a God.' Similarly, one must not treat causality, the ability to be sprayed, etc., as *defining* 'real'. In fact I do not think that all real things are causes or effects. Space-time is real, and I believe this not only because curved space-time explains gravitation but also for less recondite reasons, such as that even the simple Minkowski geometry of space-time explains clock retardation. (Recall discussion of the twin paradox in chapter 2.) Nevertheless, even if all real things *were* causes or effects, 'being a cause or effect' could not give the meaning of 'real' or 'there is a', since the latter expressions are not logical predicates.

My argument for the reality of the unobservable entities postulated by theoretical physics is that it is too much to believe that the complex and messy regularities – or non-regularities – on the observational level are just *as if* the theoretical entities exist. Postulation of the theoretical entities gives a simpler and aesthetically more satisfying picture of the world. Taking simplicity and aesthetic satisfyingness as characteristic of a good explanation, the argument could be subsumed under the notion of 'argument to the best explanation'. In the same way, Sherlock Holmes believed that the butler was the murderer because this gave the only simple explanation of the observed evidence. Any other proposed explanation would strike him and the police as complicated and far-fetched – in short, improbable.

A variant of this argument (for the existence of theoretical entities) has been put in terms of the success of theories. This variant does not seem to me importantly different from the previous argument, because the success of theories is in terms of making predictions (sometimes indirectly by explaining the predictive success of less general theories) and such success brings with it an increase in the circumstantial evidence for the literal truth of the theories. However, this variant is worth mentioning because van Fraassen gives another explanation for the success of theories. He needs to do this because on his own view he is precluded from explanation in terms of the literal truth of theories. Van Fraassen's explanation is that theories survive in competition with other theories, and so those that survive crucial experiments or observations remain while others get discarded. This Darwinian sort of explanation does not seem to me to deal with the question of why the world should be *as if* the theoretical entities really existed. According to the realist the messiness of the observational level is offset by the discovery of an underlying simplicity.

This consideration shows that an essential premiss for my argument is that the universe is simple. I do not know how to justify this, and I am afraid that I need to accept the advantage of theft over honest toil (to use an expression of Bertrand Russell's in another context) and put this up as a postulate. Note that I am talking of *ontological* simplicity. Neither realists nor anti-realists would deny the *pragmatic* advantages of simple theories. (Though this should not be exaggerated. The general theory of relativity has a simplicity and elegance missing from Newtonian theory because of its geometrical explanation of gravitation. Nevertheless, it is the classical theory, developed from Newton's, that needs to be used for practical purposes, e.g. to calculate the nautical almanac. The general theory of relativity is too mathematically intractable for such a purpose.)

It is easy to see how a liking for simple theories may have developed in biological evolution by natural selection. If we stopped to consider whether a particular snake was of a poisonous species we might get bitten. So it is useful to treat all snakes as dangerous. Since it is only a tiny time in evolutionary history that real theorizing has come into being, there cannot be an evolutionary explanation for the success of simple theories in natural science, though it may partially explain our liking for such theories. The example of the snakes drives a wedge between usefulness and truth, though on the whole there surely must on the practical level be some positive correlation between the two things.

Of course there are examples in which simplicity is not useful. It is obviously useful to test our theories when there is time. It would be disadvantageous to believe that all fruits are nutritious, because some are poisonous. The case of the fruits is not one in which there is need to act in a hurry. So caution may arise from natural selection, but this does not mean that a liking for simplicity does not arise also.

The success of simple theories in the past does not by itself give us reason to believe that the appeal to simplicity will continue to be a good heuristic for abstract and advanced physical theories. That it has been a good heuristic *hitherto* may perhaps be partly explained by the fact that heuristics, no less than theories, evolve by a sort of (non-biological) selection process. Witness the rejection of causality in quantum mechanics and the survival of extremal principles in general relativity. Nevertheless, this consideration can work both for and against the realist: not only realism but also instrumentalism or positivism (cf. Heisenberg's motivation for inventing matrix mechanics) has helped with the development of theories.

Van Fraassen has argued that the appeal to simplicity even works *against* realism. Thus he points out that the realist about entities of a theory $T$ is committed to the conjunction of two propositions: (1) theory $T$ is empirically adequate; (2) theory $T$ is true. Van Fraassen asserts only (1) while remaining agnostic about (2). Now the conjunction of (1) and (2) cannot be simpler or more probable than one of the conjuncts alone.

Of course one cannot deny that the probability of the conjunction of (1) and (2) cannot be greater than (indeed will be less than) the probability of (1) alone. However, let $p$ be the proposition that there really are the theoretical entities. (This is what (2) says over and above what (1) says.) Let $q$ be the proposition that the world is *as if* there are the theoretical entities. Let $r$ be the proposition that the universe is simple. Then it seems to me that the conditional probability of ($p$ and $q$) relative to $r$ is greater than the conditional probability of (not-$p$ and $q$) relative to $r$. (Hence unfortunately the vital necessity of $r$ for my philosophical position.)

I have to confess that I am so attracted to $r$ that realism seems to me to have an overwhelming advantage over van Fraassen's agnosticism. This is partly because my interest in science is mainly metaphysical, and not primarily for its practical advantages for technology, medicine, agriculture, and so on. In this way many scientists are metaphysicians too. Empirical adequacy is not enough for me. This of course is not an *argument*. Van Fraassen could reasonably point out that there are many things that we want but cannot have. The necessity for an ontological appeal to simplicity is what worries me most in defending realism. Let me now mention some other difficulties for realism.

The first difficulty comes from the fact that theories get overturned and replaced by others. So will not electrons one day go the way of the Ptolemaic celestial spheres or the phlogiston of eighteenth-century theorizing about combustion or the ether of nineteenth-century electrodynamics? I have for long thought that philosophers of science have greatly exaggerated this problem. Many of them have pursued philosophy of science in close connection with the history of science. Contemporary and recent historians of science have understandably been keen to oppose the old idea of the progress of science as an infallible brick by brick cumulation. They have stressed the creativity and imaginativeness of theory construction. Laudable though this is, I think that these historians of science have gone too much to the other extreme. For example, exciting discoveries in nuclear field theory have little or no effect on the quantum theory of atomic spectra, and the latter has practically no effect on protein chemistry. And so on. Science has been in modern times much more cumulative than historians of science, such as Kuhn, may tempt us to think, notwithstanding the many good insights of these historians. The existence of conceptual revolution is not completely antithetical to the existence of cumulation.

No matter what strange new things the physicists of the next generation will tell us about electrons, will they ever reject the thesis that a hydrogen atom has one proton and one electron, or that the sea, rivers and lakes on planet Earth are largely constituted of $H_2O$ molecules? J. J. Thomson had a different, because classical, concept of the electron from that of Born or Dirac. Nevertheless, there are still many sentences containing the word 'electron' which all three of these scientists would accept and which are still accepted. Looking back on the theory used by Thomson, from the vantage-point of present quantum theory, we can surely say that the predicate '. . . is an electron' as used by Thomson is true of the very same objects of which the predicate '. . . is an electron' in quantum mechanics is true. We can also see that many of Thomson's assertions about these objects (e.g. about the ratio of charge to mass, which he was the first to measure) are either true or else at least approximately true. In a mature science, such as has existed from the late nineteenth century, there is no reason to suppose that for the most part the things we assert to exist now will not continue to be asserted to exist, and that our present theories will not be regarded as at least an approximation to the truth. If this is agreed we have drawn the teeth of the objection from theory change. If it had been the case that all or most theories would later be shown to be not even approximately true then at any stage we would indeed have no reason to believe in the reality of entities postulated at that stage. I also suspect that the sorts of examples of theory change used by historians of science to oppose the cumulative picture of science are often very untypical of mature science.

### QUANTUM MECHANICS

The other main problem for a realist philosophy of science that I want to discuss in this chapter is that of reconciling realism with quantum mechanics. The formalism of quantum mechanics is well understood, and physicists of different philosophical persuasions get the same answers and use the formalism in the same way. It is undeniable that physicists differ in the interpretation of this formalism. Quantum mechanics has paradoxical features which have led many physicists to reject realism. The difficulties in giving a realist interpretation have seemed to some scientists and philosophers to have been brought to a head by a theorem due to J. S. Bell and experiments in connection with it. These investigations have been taken to rule out any possible 'hidden variable' interpretation. Hidden variable theories deny that it is ever right to say that the value of an observable, when not in a position to be measured, is unsharp or fuzzy, or that it is meaningless to talk of its value at all. They hold that the properties have sharp real number values in all circumstances. The unsharpness or fuzziness according to hidden variable theories is in our knowledge (or rather ignorance). Such theories hold that quantum mechanics is no more obscure than is classical statistical mechanics. However, though hidden variable theories would have been congenial to the philosophical realist, we must not assume that hidden variable theories are necessary for the defence of realism. Certainly the wildest conclusions have been drawn from the paradoxes of quantum mechanics, and in particular from Bell's theorem and the associated experimental investigations. Thus some physicists have drawn subjectivist conclusions, holding that things exist only when we observe them. This reminds one of Ronald Knox's limerick about the tree in the quad, apropos of Berkeley's philosophy:

> There was a young man who said 'God
> Must think it exceedingly odd
> If he finds that this tree
> Continues to be
> When there's no one about in the Quad.'

I'm not sure whether such a physicist would say that God's supernatural observation could ensure the continued existence of the tree, it being unclear whether a supernatural observation would on this hypothesis create quantum mechanical reality. Since presumably supernatural observation would involve no physical interaction, perhaps the answer is in the negative, in which case, there would be no tree for God to observe in the quad, contrary to a supplementary limerick of Ronald Knox's, in which God says that the tree does continue to be, because he is always about in the quad. Assuming the negative answer, or else leaving God out of it, the subjectivist interpretation of quantum mechanics is surely a paradox greater than those of quantum mechanics itself. How would one fit all this in with biology? With the theory of evolution? With the astronomy and geology of eras before there were conscious beings at all? How would neurophysiology be possible? How would the biochemistry of consciousness (and for that matter of anaesthesia) go, if a person's brain might exist only when he or she was conscious? We are higher mammals. Consciousness is inside the animals, not the animals inside consciousness. What about causality? Must we say, as the cosmologist J. A. Wheeler has suggested, that the big bang from which the universe originated, exists only because conscious beings evolved to know about it, so that the origin of the solar system was due in part to retro-causation from subsequent consciousness of it on the part of astronomers who exist thousands of millions of years later?

The discussions of mind and consciousness in chapter 4 and 5 will indicate why I hope for a non-subjectivist interpretation of quantum mechanics. If the experts on the subject agreed with one another on what is the right way to interpret quantum mechanics, then I, as a philosopher, could defer to the experts. Unfortunately, however, there is no such agreement. I have mentioned quantum mechanical subjectivism mainly in order to give a sense of the metaphysical excitement generated by the issues arising out of Bell's theorem. But subjectivist interpretations of quantum mechanics have in any case been popular among theoreticians long before Bell wrote.

Consider the well-known 'two-slit' experiment. As in figure 7 particles (electrons or photons) are emitted from the source $S$ towards a screen $Y$ in which are two nearby slits. (In the case of electrons the slits would in fact be interstices in a crystal. This is because the electron, considered as a wave phenomenon, is of much shorter wavelength than is a photon, and so ordinary slits will not do.) The particles reach the photo-sensitive screen $Z$ and blackening on the screen is observed to show the diffraction pattern familiar from classical optics. The highest peak (greatest blackening) is at $C$. The peaks correspond to places where the straight line paths from $A$ and $B$ differ by even numbers of half wavelengths, and the troughs where they correspond to places where the paths differ by odd numbers of half wavelengths. So it looks as though the particles are really waves. Nature has a surprise in store. If the intensity of radiation is gradually reduced, eventually single particles will be observed striking $Z$. It looks as though the electron or photon is really a particle.

Classically, if the electron or photon went through slit $A$ or $B$ alone it would end up in the region of $D$ or $E$. However, it

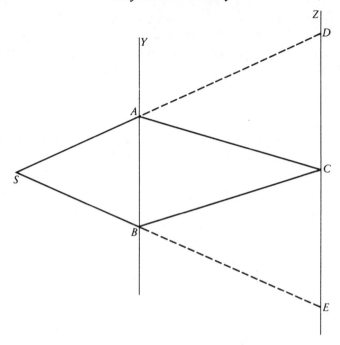

*Figure 7*  Two-slit experiment

is discovered that this happens only if the other slit is shut. This is puzzling because if it goes through *A* what should the question of a slit somewhere else (i.e. *B*) have to do with it? It would if the 'particle' were a spreading wave, but we have seen that there is experimental objection to this.

If we get a scintillation or a blackening on a particular place on the screen *Z* we can say that the particle is definitely there. Until this moment it does not seem to be definitely anywhere. In particular, we cannot suppose any definite trajectory between *S* and a place on *Z*.

Niels Bohr, whose interpretation of quantum mechanics became almost orthodox, argued that it was meaningless to talk of the position of the particle unless there was a position measurement, a 'measurement' consisting of an interaction with a macroscopic object (for example, the experimental arrangement of figure 7). Physicists came to talk of 'the collapse of the Schrödinger wave', which occurs when the particle interacts with the screen, and quantum mechanical 'position' came to be seen as a relation to a macroscopic object (in this case the experimental arrangement). A very different experimental arrangement would make the momentum of a particle definite. Bohr and his disciples thus held that it was meaningless to talk of the values of position and momentum together, or indeed of either in the absence of interaction with a macroscopic object, which had to be understood classically.

In this way quantum mechanics became to some extent parasitic on classical physics, which is unsatisfactory. Should not the experimental arrangement (in principle) be understandable classically? Consider the combined system of particle plus experimental arrangement. According to Bohr's point of view the properties of this combined system will have to be understood in relation to another macroscopic system outside it. Then if we consider a wider macroscopic system including the second one the problem recurs. And so on. Now what about the Schrödinger wave of the whole universe? By definition there is nothing outside it. What about the properties of the early universe when everything was a plasma and before there were solid (macroscopic) objects? Would the properties of this plasma have to be understood in terms of interactions with macroscopic objects very much later in time?

It is clear that this interpretation of quantum mechanics fits in very well with the sort of anti-realism propounded by van Fraassen. So if we are to stick with realism, as I have argued we should, we have two main choices. (1) We might despair of quantum mechanics as ontologically serious, and regard it as a useful dodge which will ultimately be replaced by an ontologically serious theory, much as the success of the Ptolemaic theory was explained by the more believable Copernican one. (2) We look for an interpretation of quantum mechanics which is compatible with realism.

There is another feature of quantum mechanics which may be thought to support van Fraassen. As van Fraassen points out, the so-called 'axioms' of quantum mechanics do look very much like the specification of a model, rather than like axioms in the sense of Euclid or of Newton. The reason for this is partly that the properties of quantum mechanical systems are related to an abstract multidimensional space, Hilbert space, in what at first may look a rather artificial manner. Certainly a Hilbert space is not a real physical space in the way that space-time is a real physical entity. The realist can believe in the existence of non-spatial and non-temporal entities and entities that are not causes and effects. Recall the discussion at the end of chapter 2. This is on the assumption that a nominalist account of mathematics is not possible. Hartry Field, in his book *Science without Numbers*, has attempted such an account, though he needs an ontology of space-time points. Even if such an attempt is successful, it will be no skin off the realist's nose. The realist would indeed like to disbelieve in purely mathematical objects if he or she could. To relate physical laws to an abstract mathematical space is to do nothing very different from relating physical phenomena to numbers, as when we say that if $F$ is the real number which is the force in newtons on a particle and $m$ is the real number which is its mass in kilogrammes and $f$ is the real number which is its acceleration in seconds per second, then $F = mf$ (which expresses a relation between real numbers). ('Real number' is of course used here with 'real' in the mathematical sense, not the philosophical sense of the word.) So I am not too worried about having to talk of Hilbert space. Nor am I too worried about the model theoretic look of the so-called axioms of quantum mechanics. Indeed it is probably necessary to specify classical mechanics model theoretically too. The difference between the realist and the anti-realist is that the realist holds that one of the possible models is the real world.

To return to the question of the Schrödinger wave of the whole universe. Some eminent physicists have taken it that what collapses the wave packet is not interaction with a macroscopic measuring instrument but the consciousness of the observer. They think of consciousness as outside the physical universe. They are assuming a mind–body dualism similar to that propounded in the seventeenth century by René Descartes. In chapter 5 I shall argue for the materiality of consciousness. At the very least it is hard to see how the dualistic interpretation of quantum mechanics fits in with biology and modern psychology. This attempt to make quantum mechanical properties relate not to macroscopic physical properties but to totally non-physical properties surely raises more mysteries than it solves, and makes physics as dubious as parapsychology.

I think that the realist can say that 'non-commuting' properties, such as those of position and momentum, do exist together but must say that they cannot both have real number values, and if no measurement is made neither will have a real number value. (Here take measurement broadly as covering all interactions with macroscopic entities.) The realist need not accept a 'hidden variable' theory, which would postulate sharp values in all circumstances. What to say is not clear. In his book *Incompleteness, Nonlocality and Realism*, Michael Redhead discusses three main interpretations of quantum mechanics. Two of them are that of hidden variable theories and the view associated with Copenhagen and Niels Bohr. The third is realism. He suggests that the quantum mechanical properties that the realist may describe as having 'unsharp or fuzzy values', in the case when there is no collapse of the Schrödinger wave, do not really have definite values at all but are propensities. These are manifested in relation to experimental arrangements but exist all along, just as the fragility of a glass window pane exists even when it is not being manifested by the impact of a stone. Fragility of the window pane is not an ultimate propensity, since it depends on the molecular constitution of the glass, and so would depend on further propensities of the atoms and molecules of the glass. If this is not to go on for ever we must come to ultimate propensities. Redhead suggests that the quantum mechanical properties might be such ultimate propensities. (Hidden variable theorists would deny this: the hidden variables would be like the molecular constitution of the glass.) The quantum mechanical propensities would be probabilistic: propensities not for something always to happen in identical circumstances, but for there to be a certain probability of something happening. Perhaps this is a way out, a way of accepting realism without being committed to hidden variable theories.

It is true that ultimate propensities are peculiar objects, and some may hold that to accept realism at the cost of admitting ultimate propensities is to pay too high a price. Consider the law that electrons and protons mutually attract one another, as it was stated a good many years ago, when it was believed that electrons and protons were the ultimate constituents of the universe. To say that a proton has a propensity to attract an electron may seem to be saying no more than that for any $x$ and $y$ if $x$ is a proton and $y$ is an electron then $x$ attracts $y$. The case is worse than the well-known one of the dormitive virtue. To say that a substance has a dormitive virtue is to say more than that its ingestion is followed by sleepiness. It is to point to the existence of a perhaps unknown chemical constitution, whereby, if we knew it, the induction of sleepiness might be explained. On our historical supposition, the mutual attraction of protons and electrons is supposed to be taken as an ultimate fact, and what could this be over and above the actual cases of electrons and protons attracting one another?

So to make the attribution of propensities non-vacuous we need a full blooded theory of properties as part of our ontology. This might not be a bad thing, though I am not sure how to work such a theory out in detail. After all, such properties as spin, mass, charge, charm and so on do seem to be used as explanatory in modern physics: it seems a little artificial to treat physicists' talk of these as referring only to the corresponding predicates ('has spin', etc.), linguistic entities.

W. V. Quine has objected to the ordinary philosophical notion of 'property' because of its connection with notions such as 'meaning', 'synonymy' and 'necessity', which he regards as dubious. However, the properties with which I am concerned here are not these bad old properties to which Quine rightly objects: they are postulated as theoretical entities and their introduction has nothing to do with notions of meaning and the like. Thus in saying that a body $x$ has a mass in grammes of $y$ we no longer treat 'has a mass of grammes of $y$' as a predicate but treat 'a mass in grammes of $y$' as a name of a property and 'has' as a dyadic predicate, or better still treat '. . . has . . . of . . .' as a triadic predicate relating a body, a hypothesized property and a real number. At any rate, I think we need some such expedient, with an ontology that includes properties, if we are to allow ultimate propensities, not grounded in inner structure, as explanatory.

The propensities of which Redhead speaks are, it must be remembered, probabilistic ones. They are manifested not in something always happening, but in the probability of something happening, which is tested by seeing whether a certain proportion of a wider class of things happen, i.e. whether a certain statement of relative frequency holds good within certain limits.

Let us now have a look at the philosophical issues raised by Bell's theorem and associated experiments which have sometimes been held to refute realism. Bell exploits a modification of a thought experiment proposed by Einstein, Podolsky and Rosen in 1935, who curiously enough were concerned with the *defence* of realism. Consider two particles ejected in opposite directions from an atom, these particles being of a sort that permit of two values of a quantum state called 'spin', these values being $+\frac{1}{2}$ and $-\frac{1}{2}$, or vice versa. According to the Bohr interpretation of quantum mechanics, in the absence of the measuring device the particle has no definite spin: the measurement 'throws' the particle into the state of spin $+\frac{1}{2}$ or spin $-\frac{1}{2}$ as the case may be. And according to this interpretation this 'throws' the other particle into a state of spin $-\frac{1}{2}$ or $+\frac{1}{2}$ respectively. The experiments are done in the laboratory, but in principle the right-hand detector might be in Sydney and the left-hand one in Oxford, say. How can an experiment done in Sydney simultaneously determine a state of a particle in Oxford? (Recalling chapter 2, the reader may pertinently wonder about 'simultaneously' too, since in special relativity this is relative to a frame of reference. However, I shall shelve this problem for the moment.)

Einstein's answer was that the states of a particle, even when these states are not being measured, must have sharp values, that is, that there must be 'hidden variables' that determine the evolution of the system, so that the states that determine spin $+\frac{1}{2}$ of one particle in Oxford (say) determine a spin $-\frac{1}{2}$ of the other particle at one and the same time in Sydney (say). We may suppose, however, that they do not determine these things completely, but only probabilistically: that there will be a certain probability of the left particle being in state $+\frac{1}{2}$ (or $-\frac{1}{2}$). Nevertheless, when the right particle *is* in one state, the other particle must be in the opposite state and vice versa. Thus if there are spin detectors in position to measure the spin of the right particle and the spin of the left particle there will be 100 per cent correlation: $\pm\frac{1}{2}$ spin detected on the right will correlate with $\mp$ spin detected on the left.

It has so far been assumed that the spin detectors are in the straight line in the directions in which the particles are emitted. Suppose that the spin detectors are swung round so as to be at equal and opposite angles between $0°$ and $90°$ to this straight line. According to classical ideas they would measure spins between 0 and $\mp\frac{1}{2}$. However, in quantum mechanics the spin can take only (positive or negative) integral multiples of $\frac{1}{2}$ as values. Let $\theta$ be the angle between the two detectors. A proportion $\frac{1}{2}\cos^2\theta/2$ will be found in the right-hand detector to have spin $+\frac{1}{2}$ and a proportion $\frac{1}{2}\cos^2\theta/2$ will be found in the left-hand detector to have spin $-\frac{1}{2}$. (And vice versa.) But what about the correlation between spin $+\frac{1}{2}$ in the right-hand detector and spin $-\frac{1}{2}$ simultaneously in the left-hand detector?

Bell proved a theorem in the form of an inequality, which is therefore often termed 'Bell's inequality'. This inequality would hold if the amount of correlation was due to the probability of spin $+\frac{1}{2}$ in the right-hand experiment correlating with spin $-\frac{1}{2}$ in the left-hand experiment because they depended (perhaps probabilistically) on earlier sharp values of the spin when the atoms shot out particles in opposite directions originally. Bell also showed that if Bohr's idea that the spin variables did not have sharp values in the absence of experimental determination of them was correct, the correlation would be greater for certain infinite classes of values of the variable $\theta$. A variety of experiments of this general sort seem to have confirmed Bohr's point of view against Einstein's.

Are we to accept the subjectivist conclusion from this that the tree in the quad does not exist when no one observes it? I think not. There are too many loopholes in the argument, if it is supposed to have this strange conclusion.

(1) Bell's argument requires as a premiss an axiom of locality, to the effect that there is no sort of action at a distance, whereby what happens in an experiment at a space–time point $X$ cannot affect what happens at a space–time point $Y$ where $XY$ lies entirely outside a light cone (cf. chapter 2). (Thus $X$ and $Y$ will be simultaneous in some suitable inertial frame of reference.) The arbitrariness of simultaneity in special relativity makes this locality principle very plausible: if there is action at a distance, we may ask just what set of axes in Minkowski space determines the simultaneity of the events $X$ and $Y$. (Action at a distance did not raise this problem for Newton because simultaneity for him was absolute.)

Even so, locality *could* be denied. There might be a preferred set of inertial axes in Minkowski space. It might even be singled out by cosmological considerations, as a frame of reference in which the cosmic background radiation (a legacy of the 'big bang' from which the universe originated) is equal in all directions. Admittedly this would be worrying, as electromagnetic and mechanical phenomena would be Lorentz invariant and Bell type phenomena would not be Lorentz invariant, but it would not be impossible.

(2) Even though non-commuting quantum mechanical variables might not simultaneously have sharp values, in the way Einstein wanted to argue that they would (or any variables in the absence of an experiment), something might be made of Redhead's suggestion of real propensities, as discussed earlier in this chapter.

(3) Even on the Bohr view, the tree in the quad could exist when no one saw it, if one did not combine this view with mind–body dualism and if one merely regarded an experiment as an interaction with a macroscopic object. After all the tree itself is a macroscopic object, and most sub-atomic events within or even on the surface of the tree will result in interactions with parts of the tree itself. So we could also say that the sub-atomic entities of which the tree consists exist even when no one sees the tree or does an experiment there. (However, this consideration would not remove worries about the objective reality of the cosmic plasma at the time of the big bang, when there were no macroscopic objects in the ordinary sense of these words.)

(4) Theoretical physicists seem to disagree with one another on the interpretation of quantum mechanics as much as philosophers do on issues of realism and idealism. The whole situation, from the outside, seems extremely confused. Until it settles down we should abstain from rash inferences to subjectivism. Especially when this would raise even greater problems for the interpretation of geology, palaeontology, evolutionary biology, and other sciences. The main purpose of the last few pages has, however, been to avoid disguising from the reader that quantum mechanics does raise puzzles

and paradoxes that at least raise *difficulties* for someone, such as myself, who wishes to defend a realist metaphysics.

### SUGGESTIONS FOR FURTHER READING AND BIBLIOGRAPHICAL REFERENCES

A useful collection of papers for and against realism about theoretical entities in Jarrett Leplin (ed. with an introduction), *Scientific Realism* (Berkeley: University of California Press, 1984). An excellent introduction, in a manner intelligible to the layman, to quantum mechanics and its various possible interpretations is Alastair I. M. Rae, *Quantum Physics: illusion or reality?* (Cambridge: Cambridge University Press, 1986). A much more technical work is Michael Redhead, *Incompleteness, Nonlocality and Realism: a prolegomenon to the philosophy of quantum mechanics* (Oxford: Clarendon Press, 1987). A relevant book, aimed not only at physicists but also at general philosophical readers (there are technical appendices), is Henry Krips, *The Metaphysics of Quantum Theory* (Oxford: Oxford University Press, 1987). Its object is to defend realism while yet avoiding the traditional difficulties of hidden variable theories. Peter Forrest in his *Quantum Metaphysics* (Oxford: Basil Blackwell, 1988) suggests three possible (realist) speculative interpretations of quantum mechanics. An easy introduction to model theory may be found in J. N. Crossley, C. J. Ash, C. J. Brickhill, J. C. Stillwell and N. H. Williams, *What is Mathematical Logic* (Oxford: Oxford University Press, 1972), chapter 3. A witty and instructive article on Bell's inequality is N. David Mermin, 'Quantum Mysteries for Anyone', *Journal of Philosophy*, 78 (1981), 397–408. A theory of propensities is propounded in D. H. Mellor, *The Matter of Chance* (Cambridge: Cambridge University Press, 1971).

Other references are as follows: A. S. Eddington, *The Nature of the Physical World* (Cambridge: Cambridge University Press, 1928); L. S. Stebbing, *Philosophy and the Physicists* (London: Methuen, 1937); Brandon Carter, 'The Anthropic Principle and its Implications for Biological Evolution', *Phil. Trans. Royal Society of London*, A310 (1983), 347–63, especially p. 352; W. V. Quine and J. S. Ullian, *The Web of Belief*, rev. edn (New York: Random House, 1978); Bas C. van Fraassen, *The Scientific Image* (Oxford:

Clarendon Press, 1980); Ian Hacking, *Representing and Intervening* (Cambridge: Cambridge University Press, 1983), especially p. 23; Ernst Mach, *The Analysis of Sensations*, translated by C. M. Williams, revised and supplemented from the 5th German edition by S. Waterlow, and with new introduction by T. S. Szasz (New York: Dover, 1959).

# 4

# Biology, Psychology and Intentionality

## PHYSICALISM

In the last chapter I was concerned to argue for a realist account of physics. In the present chapter and the following one I shall be concerned to argue that there is nothing in the world over and above the entities of physics, and that everything operates according to the laws of physics. According to this view, living organisms (including human beings) are very complicated physical mechanisms and nothing more. Of course it is liable to cause misunderstanding if we say 'human beings are *only* very complicated physical mechanisms.' Stressing the 'only' may divert our audience from metaphysical contemplation to irrelevant questions of value judgement. In saying that humans are 'only' very complicated physical mechanisms I intend only to make an ontological point – a point about the make up of the universe. It is not to deny that some complicated physical mechanisms do very wonderful things. Some have written symphonies, others have erected gothic cathedrals, others have penetrated the secrets of the atom, and others yet again have erected beautiful edifices of pure mathematics. A physicalist metaphysics of course does not deny any of this. Indeed, to say that a leaf of a tree, or even a single living cell, is *only* a complicated physical mechanism can be taken wrongly. A physicalist is well aware of the extraordinary complexity of a living cell and even more of a whole leaf of a tree, orders of awesome complexity far and away above that of any human artefact of the sort that our aesthetic colleagues enthuse about.

The 'only' in 'only a very complex physical mechanism' is an ontological one, and neutral about value. It takes no sides about what we find most admirable: some may prefer to immerse themselves in contemplation of the leaf, others of the cathedral or the symphony.

Some will object to the physicalist thesis on a different score. They will say that the thesis is trivial. Suppose, for example, and contrary to fact, that biology needed to postulate a vital force. Then it might be said that such a vital force would be just another of the fundamental forces of nature, and so its investigation would be part of an expanded physics. Thus it could be objected that if I say that the objects of biological and psychological investigation are only complicated physical mechanisms, I have said nothing of interest.

I propose to avoid this sort of objection in the following way. For the purposes of discussing biology and psychology I shall identify physics with present-day physics. In doing this I shall not deny that there will be revolutionary changes in physics. Nevertheless, discoveries about quarks, black holes, theories of strings and superstrings, and so on will have no impact on biology and psychology. For example, the properties of the brain are those of assemblages of neurons, and the study of the neuron requires only quite well-known physics and chemistry, which will not be overthrown, at least to the required degree of approximation, by future revolutions. As I noted on p. 64, the reaction against Whiggish history of science, the view of science as brick by brick cumulation, has gone too far, insightful though much of the recent work on scientific revolutions has been. The physicist Gerald Feinberg, in a well-known article, has indeed argued that the theory of the electron, proton, neutron, neutrino and photon and their anti-particles, when they have such, is enough to explain the properties of 'ordinary matter'. (Not what goes on inside neutron stars or inside black holes, or the behaviour of the transitory particles created only with big cyclotrons.) Feinberg thus holds that the 'Thales Problem' (of what the world of familiar objects is made of) has essentially been solved. (Thales is commonly regarded as the first Greek philosopher. He lived around 600 BC and propounded the question of what everything is made of. He gave arguments, quite plausible at the time, that it was water.) Now you and I are familiar objects and if, say, telepathy existed and was not explicable in terms of the forces known to contemporary physics, then we would have to say that Feinberg was not quite right. Thus Feinberg's thesis is by no means trivial. Nor is physicalism as I have defined it.

Physicalism may be characterized as a reductionist thesis. However, it is reductionist in an ontological sense, not as a thesis that all statements can be *translated* into statements about physical particles, and so on. This is partly because many words used by biologists, or in common sense contexts, such as 'tree', are taught and learned partly ostensively, for example by having trees pointed out to us, or perhaps just by hearing of the word 'tree' uttered in suitable tree-rich surroundings. This does not show that trees are not complex physical mechanisms.

Another, and perhaps more significant objection to translational reduction arises if we look at chemistry, which is already well integrated with physics through the physical theory of the chemical bond. (The physics of valency.) Indeed there are various types of chemical bond (the bond that joins atoms together to form molecules). Thus the electrovalent bond in simple cases can be understood well enough in terms of classical physics. (This is the bond which joins atoms of sodium and chlorine so as to form the familiar crystals of table salt.) On the other hand, the covalent bond, which depends on the sharing of electrons between atoms, requires the quantum mechanical idea of resonance, whereby an atom can be (say) 50 per cent in each of two incompatible states.

Are chemical laws reducible to physical ones? I would say that the ability of physicists to explain the chemical bond in simple cases enables us to assert as a plausible metaphysical conjecture that it is only problems of computation and the necessity to make simplifying assumptions that usually prevents us from deducing chemical facts from physical ones. Thus we are up against the problems associated with the *n*-body problem in quantum mechanics. Even in classical mechanics the *n*-body problem can be solved only by approximative methods. (This is a matter of mathematical principle, not merely of practical difficulty.) In classical mechanics the *n*-body problem can be resistant even to approximative methods, though the wonderful success and accuracy of predictions in celestial mechanics (the mechanics of Sun and planets) is noteworthy. Celestial mechanics is made easier by the fact that the Sun is so much more massive than even Jupiter, the largest planet, and by the relatively small number of bodies involved. In valency theory physicists have to contend with the fact that when dealing with large atoms they are up against immense difficulties with the *n*-body problem in quantum mechanics and the approximative assumptions that need to be made. These tax the greatest computers. Indeed one may wonder whether certain computations could be too much for even the largest physically possible computer. Suppose that a computer the size of the galaxy would not be big enough. Indeed if one the size of the galaxy were possible, signals even at the speed of light between its components would take too long. Remember that a light signal would take 60,000 years to traverse the galaxy. If the computer were squashed together to eliminate this problem it would collapse gravitationally, and perhaps become a neutron star. I think that we had better stop talking of computations 'in principle'.

What it is for chemistry to be ontologically reducible to physics, even though one cannot deduce all statements of chemistry from statements of physics, is this: any model of a set of true sentences of chemistry will be a model of a set of true sentences of physics. One can assert this as a plausible metaphysical conjecture on the basis of the success, such as it is, of the quantum theory of valency, together with plausible explanations of lack of success in terms of computational and approximative difficulties.

However, in what follows, when I discuss biology, I shall be content enough to make my discussion independently of this thesis, talking of 'physics and chemistry', without worrying about the ontological reducibility of chemistry to physics, even though for my general metaphysical picture of the world, the ontological reducibility of chemistry to physics is indeed of importance to me.

## BIOLOGY

There are explanations in biology which are straightforward descriptions of how a certain sort of physical system works. This is obviously the case in the chemical explanations of photosynthesis and of respiration. Such explanations belong to what for present purposes I shall take to be the central core of biology, the biochemical one. Many of the explanations of the functioning of cells, for example those belonging to the human liver or kidney, explanations of neural transmission, and explanations of the forming of protein molecules as a result of interactions, within the cell, involving the nucleic acids DNA and RNA, are of this sort. Sometimes what has to be explained is the *function* of an organ. Typical organs look *as if* they had been designed for a purpose; for example, the eye looks as if it had been designed to send visual information to the brain. However, we should not think that organs actually *have* been designed. The explanation of why an organ looks *as if* it had been designed to perform a function comes from the theory of natural selection. Organs have evolved, often in a haphazard and opportunistic way, and as a result of natural selection they give the *appearance* of design. This is quite compatible with a physicalist ontology. The abstract theory of self-reproducing robots has been well worked out, originally in a well-known paper by the great mathematician J. von Neumann. Now what a robot can do presumably carbon-based life can do too on purely physical principles. Indeed there are now mechanistic accounts of how the double helix of DNA replicates itself, how genetic information is coded in it and how this information is transmitted chemically so as to influence the development of the embryo. In principle von Neumann robots could evolve by natural selection: bullets or cosmic ray particles might change their programming, just as a genetic mutation in a living organism might occur due to some chance influence. Mutations due to an unnecessary lot of X-ray examinations might lead to a genetic defect in some future children. I say 'defect' because it is easier to go wrong than to go right: some mutations lead to enhanced biological fitness – i.e. adaptability to an environment – but harmful mutations vastly outnumber the useful ones.

Because of the background theory of evolution by natural selection it is clearly a useful methodology for a scientist trying to understand a particular organ (whether familiar ones such as ears or eyes or unfamiliar ones such as mitochondria, which are small organelles in the interior of cells) to ask himself or herself: 'How would the relevant function be best achieved?' The scientist may be able to verify that some structure or mechanism or chemical constitution which would help to bring about such a function is indeed present. Such teleological thinking has nothing mysterious or anti-mechanistic about it. (To mark the distinction between teleology in the sense of purposiveness and the 'as if' teleology explicable by natural selection one might follow the biologist Ernst Mayr and give up the word 'teleology' in the latter context and use instead the term 'teleonomy', though I shall not follow him here, preferring to trust the reader to rely on context for the proper understanding of my references to teleology.)

Such teleological thinking indeed helps the biologist to locate mechanisms: it is no substitute for mechanistic explanation in the way that Aristotelian teleology was meant to be. The sort of teleological thinking that is characteristic of the modern biologist is a heuristic handmaiden of mechanistic explanation, not an enemy of it.

Nor need the heuristics assume that a function is performed in the best possible way, as had been supposed by traditional pre-Darwinian theologians, for example William Paley, who thought that organisms must have been designed by an omnipotent God, just as a watch might be designed by a watchmaker. Natural selection is opportunistic, and bodily parts that performed some functions in earlier species may become modified and adapted to other functions in later species. The extraordinary story of the evolution of the ear is a case in point. Indeed evolution by natural selection can sometimes explain apparent bad design no less than it can explain apparent good design. A striking example of this is the case of the human sinuses. Anyone who has suffered from the excruciating pain of sinusitis, due to infection and inflammation of the membranes that constitute the linings of the sinuses beside our noses, will regret the fact that our lower sinuses have their openings at the top, not at the bottom, so that they do not drain well, and infection builds up. This is explained by the fact that humans evolved from four footed creatures, which held their heads down, and natural selection ensured that the drain holes were appropriately placed for them. Not for us, however, because of our upright stance.

Nevertheless, notwithstanding such defects, biological systems on the whole have a very great reliability. Your body or mine contains something of the order of $10^{14}$ living cells. Very few out of this vast number become defective, and if there are mutations or other accidents that cause them to become defective in such a way as to affect us as a whole (in particular if they become cancerous) they are usually killed off by appropriate antibodies. Both the reliability and the occasional partial maladaptation (as in the case of the sinuses) have a good explanation in terms of evolution by natural selection.

Consider what I proposed to take as the central core of

biology, the biochemical investigation into the functioning of cells and arrays of cells. Very near this central core are more abstract studies of cells or complicated arrays of cells in which these are treated somewhat as 'black boxes'. A biochemical explanation of the functioning is no doubt supposed to be somehow in the offing, even though too difficult, either in practice or in principle, or perhaps simply not germane to the investigation at hand.

In talking of the biochemical or near or partly biochemical core of biology as 'central', I am not using this in any normative sense. Thus some people quite legitimately think of the theory of evolution as the central core of biology. Moreover, the biochemical and evolutionary parts of biology are not in watertight compartments: to some extent they not only complement one another, but also interpenetrate and interact.

In the biochemical explanation of cell functioning chemistry is applied to a certain sort of natural history. This is not the casual sort of natural history that can be done with the naked eye, as when we observe that tigers have stripes. It may require observation not only with optical microscopes but with electron microscopes, a sort of observation (even in the case of optical microscopes) that requires sophisticated training and experience. It may also require chemical analysis, as, for example, when it was discovered that chromosomes contain nucleic acids. Nevertheless, what results is from a logical point of view natural history all the same. The descriptive cytologist is no more concerned to state universal laws of nature than the field naturalist is. There are certainly cells with deviant numbers of chromosomes. Nor does the cytologist need to concern himself or herself with the question of extra-terrestrial application of his or her generalizations. Perhaps a biologist may expect that if extra-terrestrial cellular life is discovered it will be organized with genetic material made up of DNA, or perhaps the biologist will not expect this. It does not matter for ordinary cytological investigations. Still less can we expect that less central details of cell functioning will hold good in extra-terrestrial cases, supposing there to be such. Other details may vary from terrestrial species to terrestrial species, or even from individual to individual.

Contrast physics, in which the laws are supposed to apply everywhere and everywhen in the universe. This last sentence perhaps requires some qualification. In chapter 7 I shall refer to speculations that what we have thought of as our universe is one of many (small 'u') universes that make up a (big 'u') Universe, and that the fundamental constants of nature vary from universe to universe. The idea is that in the first $10^{-33}$ seconds of cosmic expansion (after the 'big bang') the laws of nature were proto-laws and that the Universe crystallized into many, possibly infinitely many, small 'u' universes, with differing values of the fundamental constants of nature. Be that as it may, the contrast between physics and biology is very striking. It would not affect terrestrial biology if it were discovered that life on a distant planet had very different biochemical bases. Moreover, since organisms are very complex systems we are not surprised if some 'misbehave': for example, we do not treat genetic defects as constituting exceptions to laws. Natural history is the topic of rough generalizations, not of tight laws. Nevertheless, in order to explain the functioning of organisms biologists *do* make use of tight laws, but these laws are of physics and chemistry. It is not easy to find tight laws of a specifically biological character. These tight laws of physics and chemistry are applied to the loose generalizations of natural history in order to furnish explanations.

To illustrate and amplify this contention I wish to make a comparison between the central core of biology on the one hand and technology on the other hand. Consider a technologist who is designing some electronic device. He or she will have some understanding of how the components of the device will behave in ways somehow explicable on physical principles. Nevertheless, in thinking of his or her design he or she will not bother about these physical principles themselves, but will treat the components as black boxes that produce a certain output for a given input, or more generally will have certain characteristic curves for variable input against variable output. Again he or she may want to know, for example, that a crystal oscillates at a frequency 10mHz or that a capacitor functions reliably at frequencies between 10kHz and 20kHz. (One mHz – megahertz – is a frequency of a million cycles per second, and one kHz – kilohertz – is a frequency of one thousand cycles per second.) The designer may also be interested in other things, such as whether such components can be bought and whether they cost too much, but I shall ignore these economic matters in making my comparison between technology and biology.

The designer may to a great extent keep physical principles at the back of his or her mind. Sometimes he or she will need to bring them to the fore, and the designer of the components or 'black boxes' themselves will, unless he or she treats them as made up of smaller black boxes, need to go back to the physical principles. This will be even more the case with inventors, as opposed to designers. For example, it was physical knowledge of a very sophisticated sort that led to the invention of the transistor. In any case, even when design stops at the black box level, physical principles are needed for *understanding*. (This is epitomized by a favourite book of my youth, J. A. Ratcliffe's *Physical Principles of Wireless*.)

In the case of biology there is a primary emphasis not on design but on understanding. There is of course biotechnology, which in a sense has existed for a long time, as in the development of strains of wheat resistant to disease and so on, but has exploded recently, with the discovery of antibiotics, the development of synthetic pharmaceutical products such as sulphonamides, and nowadays the whole subject of genetic engineering. Nevertheless, biology as a science is a matter not of doing but of understanding, and yet even in this respect there is a strong analogy with physical technologies. We are surrounded by technological artefacts which condition our very way of life. Just as we wish to understand the stars in their courses, so we should surely wish to understand our telephones, radios, television sets, motor car engines, home computers, and so on. Sometimes, as with motor car engines, the motive will be partly practical, but even here the desire for understanding can still exist in someone who like me has not the aptitude to be a practical mechanic. In our technological culture surely, if we have any pride, we should not be content to treat our telephones and televisions as magical mysteries. This sort of interest in electronic and mechanical artefacts and the sort of interest that biochemically and mechanistically oriented biologists have in living systems are very similar to one another.

We could expect that if there are Alpha Centaurians and they have television sets these would have designs analogous to those of terrestrial television sets. However, we should not be too confident in this expectation. It is in no way important for our understanding of terrestrial television sets that we should hold opinions on the question of what extra-terrestrial television sets might be like. Similarly speculations about exobiology are not at all crucial for the understanding of terrestrial organisms. If a researcher is investigating some biochemical problem in human immunology, for example, he or she can afford to remain neutral as to whether extra-terrestrial life exists, whether it is carbon based and whether the genetic material consists of nucleic acids. The understanding of present life forms is largely independent of the question of the origin of terrestrial life in the first place, intellectually important though this is. I have said that the motive for understanding technology can be purely intellectual, and this is certainly the dominant motive for most fundamental research in biology, even though an interest in practical applications in medicine and agriculture has often been important too.

Just as the technologist who is designing an electronic circuit will believe that all the components he or she proposes to use will behave in accordance with the laws of physics, even while being willing to treat the components as 'black boxes', so often a biologist will think in this sort of way about components of living systems. In neither case is there a search for specifically technological or biological laws. The technologist and biologist alike will make use of more or less reliable empirical generalizations, exceptions to which are unsurprising and often explicable. If an electronic apparatus does not work in the usual way the technologist may still be confident of explaining the malfunction no less than of explaining normal behaviour, and the same applies to biology. Sometimes, indeed, it is the abnormal that points the way to understanding the normal: the importance of the study of persons with specific brain lesions is a particularly poignant but not untypical case in point, since it enables neurophysiologists to map the activities of the normal brain.

I have been discussing what I regard as the central core of biology (the biochemical and biophysical core) and have been comparing it with technology, not in respect of practical orientation but in respect of the type of understanding that is sought. In both cases the concerns are terrestrial, or even more cosmically parochial. Other writers on the philosophy of biology, such as Michael Ruse, seem to me to place the central core differently, since they put great stress on evolutionary theory. The theory of evolution, as it has come down to us, is certainly cosmically parochial. The theory of evolution is concerned to explain the fact of terrestrial evolution, a fact which seems uncontrovertible on account of the palaeontological record, incomplete and sketchy though this often is. To deny the fact one would have to adopt the heroic course of the nineteenth-century biologist Philip Gosse. In his book *Omphalos* Gosse argued that God would have created Adam with a navel, though obviously Adam would have had no need of this, and so similarly he held that when God created the earth in 4004 BC he would have created it as a going concern, with fossils in the rocks, just as if it had existed for hundreds of millions of years. Unfortunately this attempt to reconcile the book of Genesis with contemporary geological and palaeontological discoveries was not enthusiastically received either by the theologians or by Gosse's scientific colleagues.

The theory of evolution gives a possible mechanism whereby the fact of evolution could have come about. This is the theory of evolution by natural selection, now much integrated with post-Mendelian genetics and with molecular biology. Since no other plausible mechanism can be envisaged, the scientific method that the philosopher Gilbert Harman has distinguished and called 'inference to the best explanation' leads us to believe in the Darwinian theory, or rather the modern synthetic theory which relates the theory of natural selection to the hypotheses relating to genetic recombination, mutation, and linkage and interaction of genes in chromosomes. Genes were originally hypothetical entities, defined functionally, but are now thought of as segments of DNA. The modern synthesis blends the Darwinian hypothesis of natural selection with neo-Mendelian population genetics. Population genetics modified the simple theory of natural selection, including such subsidiary ideas as that of statistical genetic drift. Mendelian ideas saved Darwin's theory from a serious objection. Darwin was stuck with a notion of blending inheritance, which could not explain evolution. Darwin was forced by his belief in blending inheritance to accept Lamarckian ideas of inheritance of acquired characteristics. These Lamarckian ideas were shown later to be contrary to the empirical facts, and they are implausible anyway because there is no known physical mechanism that could go towards explaining how such inheritance of acquired characteristics could come about. (There are certain explicable phenomena that simulate Lamarkian inheritance but are not really in accordance with it.)

In so far as the theory of evolution is concerned with the history of life on our planet Earth, it is from the logical point of view a historical science, as is geology. Geology of course uses the laws of physics and chemistry to explain the historical facts in which it is interested, for example conglomerate here, granite there, lava somewhere else. The theory of evolution is integrated with genetics, and molecular genetics is connected with chemistry. However, the main basis of the theory of evolution is generally taken to be the principle of natural selection. Is this a genuine example of a biological law, or is it merely a terrestrial generalization, or is it even a mere tautology?

Philosophers often state the principle in terms of 'fitness' and then discuss whether or not the statement that the fittest survive is or is not a tautology. (Fitness here being defined in terms of reproductive advantage.) However, good biologists define the principle of natural selection (if and when they do define it) in some such terms as the following.

> In any population of organisms there is variation in individuals and some at least of this is heritable. In any particular environment some of these differences will confer greater survival value on their holders, so that they will leave more progeny. Variations in the environment sort out heritable variations in the populations.

These three sentences do not seem to add up to tautology. Perhaps the first half of the first sentence comes near to tautology, because if there is no variation one might refuse to concede that there was an organism involved: consider the way in which crystals reproduce without variation. Be this as it may, I am prepared to concede law status to this principle: one would expect it to apply also in extra-terrestrial environments everywhere and everywhen. Still, I want to say that specifically biological laws (as opposed to generalizations of terrestrial natural history) do not occur often in biology, and this does not matter. Sometimes philosophers, wedded to some concept of 'fitness', argue that due to cosmic accident, e.g. a giant meteor striking the Earth, the best adapted organisms may nevertheless not survive. But then the organisms would not *in fact* be best adapted: the meteor is a rare event but it *is* part of the environment. Some simple bacteria will survive and they will have turned out to be best adapted to the environment.

I have noticed that some philosophers of biology try to make evolutionary theory look too much like physics with some principle of 'survival of the fittest' as an axiom. On the other hand, I have noticed that a standard introductory book on evolutionary fact and theory (G. Ledyard Stebbins, *Processes of Organic Evolution*, second edition) does not explicitly state the principle of natural selection at all. So philosophically I am perhaps in some respects more in sympathy with some biologists than with some philosophers of biology. However, the important matter for my present metaphysical purposes is the demonstration of how recombination and mutation of genes, both mechanistic processes, can lead to adaptations to changing circumstances.

How did evolution, or life itself, originate? There are various theories about the ways in which macromolecules suitable to be the building blocks of life might have originated on Earth, or even in meteorites which land on earth from outer space, having originally been 'cooked' by certain purely physical processes elsewhere. Here there seems to be little firm knowledge and much speculation, but at least these considerations show that it is not impossible that life originated from inorganic matter, and in the absence of any plausible speculations about how *else* it could have come about it is reasonable, in the present state of knowledge, to believe that it did originate from purely physical processes that led to the formation of suitable macromolecules.

## PSYCHOLOGY

I now wish to say something about psychology. This is a branch of biology and much of what I said about biology is applicable here too. Scientific psychology is at bottom a study of how the brain works in causing behaviour, whether or not the study of the brain goes right down to the neural level, as in neurophysiological psychology, or whether it is in terms of

functionally described 'black boxes', which are assumed to
have some sort of neural realization, whether or not these are
anatomically distinct entities. Thus scientific psychology is
not behaviouristic. Behaviouristic psychology erred in treating the whole brain as a black box and looking for tight
stimulus–response laws. We would not try to understand
even a simple radio receiver in this behaviouristic way: even if
one were not allowed to look inside it understanding would
come from hypotheses about its internal organization, whether
at a lower 'black box' level or right down to circuitry. The
brain is so complicated, of course, that we cannot describe the
detailed circuitry as we can in the case of the radio, but
something can be said about it that may reinforce low-level
'black box' hypotheses.

Humanists may rightly say that this sort of scientific
psychology is not much use in predicting human behaviour.
In understanding how the human mind works Jane Austen
has certain obvious superiorities over professors of neurophysiological or experimental psychology. On the other
hand, scientific psychology has many surprises for even
sophisticated common sense psychology. We read of blind
people who are adamant that they can see and also of people
who can detect things in their environment visually and yet
who are adamant that they are blind. Such people have brain
lesions, but even so these factors are inconsistent with
common sense beliefs about the nature of consciousness.
These examples are taken from Paul Churchland's excellent
introductory book on the philosophy of mind *Matter and
Consciousness*. Elsewhere in the same book he cites evidence
in the field of normal psychology, evidence which shows that
we are much more unreliable in reporting beliefs, desires and
other states of mind (as judged by behavioural evidence) than
common sense leads us to believe. Common sense notions of
introspection as reliable internal perception has to some
extent to give way to thinking of our knowledge of our own
beliefs and desires as the unconscious formulation of explanatory hypotheses. A study of the psychological literature will

unearth many more surprises for common sense beliefs about the mind.

## INTENTIONALITY

With all its defects, however, common sense psychology, in which we explain actions in terms of beliefs, desires, memory, perception, anger, irritableness, complacency, optimism, pessimism, concentration, carelessness, and so on, is the best thing we have in daily life or when writing history, as when we assess character, ascribe motives and explain actions generally. However advanced scientific psychology becomes, it is hard to imagine that a future Gibbon who was writing of the decline of a civilization would use the language of scientific psychology, except in special cases. I shall therefore consider some concepts of common sense psychology, and shall concentrate on those of *belief* and *desire*. Thus if Mary turns her radio to 102 mHz it would seem to be an adequate common sense explanation of her action to say that she believed that Beethoven's Fifth Symphony was about to be broadcast on that frequency and that she desired to hear this symphony. Certain *ceteris paribus* clauses must be assumed. Mary might believe that she could hear a better performance of the symphony on her hi-fi gramophone and might have tuned her radio only in a fit of absent-mindedness. Nevertheless, the language of belief and desire is a pretty good tool for explaining and predicting human behaviour. Now what is the metaphysical significance of this? Should we identify beliefs and desires with neurophysiological states?

As a first approximation I should answer this question with 'Yes'. In ordinary common sense we do seem to think of beliefs and desires as states typically caused or partly caused by certain stimuli, or by other beliefs and desires, and also as states that typically cause certain behaviour and also other beliefs and desires. But we also think that brain states fit into the causal story in the same sort of way. So perhaps beliefs and desires just *are* brain states. Of course, though this identification may be plausible to us, it was not always so, and in certain cultural circles it may not be thought plausible nowadays. The proposition that beliefs and desires are brain states is not a trivial semantic truth such as the proposition that a bachelor is an unmarried adult male human being. It is a matter of contingent fact, like the proposition that in a certain university the professor of anatomy is identical with the dean of the medical faculty. Beliefs and desires are understood in common sense in terms of the causal roles that they undertake, and in psychology 'black boxes' are so understood too. The black boxes are supposed to have neurophysiological insides. Therefore it is plausible to identify beliefs and desires with brain states.

This is, as I said, an approximation. One reason for this qualification is connected with the way in which we identify beliefs and desires. We identify them by reference to *propositions*. To explain this I need to draw attention to certain features of the semantics of 'belief' and 'desire' locutions.

Suppose that Joe desires a bicycle. The grammatical form of 'Joe desires a bicycle' looks superficially like that of 'Joe rides a bicycle.' The similarity is deceptive. If Joe rides a bicycle there must be some particular bicycle that he rides. If he desires a bicycle there need not be some particular bicycle that he desires. Any reasonably good bicycle might do. So one cannot deduce from 'Joe desires a bicycle' the proposition 'There is a bicycle that Joe desires'. Again, suppose that Joe desires a unicorn. He thinks that it would be lovely to have a unicorn in his paddock. Unfortunately there are no unicorns. (If there are infinitely many or even very many planets suitable for life in the universe there are certain to be or pretty sure to be one-horned horse-like mammals somewhere, but read 'unicorn' here to mean 'terrestrial unicorn'. There are none of these.) So desiring a unicorn is not a bit like kicking a unicorn. If Joe kicks a unicorn there must be some unicorn that is kicked. From 'Joe kicks a unicorn' we can deduce

'There exists some unicorn such that Joe kicks it.' From 'Joe desires a unicorn' it does not follow that there exists a unicorn such that Joe desires it.

Some philosophers have talked as though the word 'desires' was after all a relational predicate but that it relates Joe not to an ordinary object but to an 'intentional object'. The Austrian philosopher Franz Brentano spoke of 'intentional inexistence', and held that what distinguished the mental from the physical was this sort of 'intentionality' and 'direction upon an object'. It is hard to make sense of this. What is the object? When I desire a unicorn I do not desire an idea or mental object of a unicorn. (I could fulfil this last desire all too easily.) And Brentano did not mean this. He contrasted physical relations with mental relations, but this is illegitimately to try to make a psychological distinction do the job that needs to be done by a logical or grammatical one. Perhaps we should just treat Brentano as usefully, indeed in a pioneering way, drawing attention to the sort of distinctions that I have made in the last paragraph.

Let us forswear, then, this mystifying talk of 'intentional objects' and seek some other way out. If we allow ourselves to depart slightly from colloquial English, we can follow Quine and say that when we talk of Joe desiring a unicorn we talk of a relation between Joe and an English sentence. (A German no doubt would talk of a relation between Joe and a German sentence.) Thus let us replace 'Joe desires a unicorn' by 'Joe desires-true "Joe possesses a unicorn".' Whether or not unicorns exist, the sentence 'Joe possesses a unicorn' surely does. (At least if we allow sets into our ontology. Sequences can be defined in terms of sets, and a sentence could be regarded as a sequence of words, and words themselves as classes of utterances of a certain sound, or something along these lines. Note that this allows us to talk of sentences that have never been uttered, since we can take it that all words of a language have been uttered, and that certain sequences of words will never have been uttered.) Moreover, there is a definite particular sentence that is desired-true: we do not have the problem that if 'desires' was a relational predicate there would have to be a particular unicorn that was desired, not just any old unicorn.

Propositions are what are commonly thought of as what are expressed by those indicative sentences that are used to make assertions or suppositions. (Not all indicative sentences are. For example, the sentence 'I name this ship the "Mary Rose"' is used to name the ship, not to report an act of naming, and the sentence 'The battalion will move at dawn' is used by the commanding officer to give an order, not to make a prediction.) So beliefs and desires are commonly thought of as 'propositional attitudes'. (So are hopes, fears, wishes, and so on.) So we could avoid the artificiality of making 'believe-true' and 'desire-true' refer to a relation to a sentence (and hence a particular language) by making them refer to a relation between a person and a proposition. However, the notion of 'what a sentence expresses' or 'the meaning of a sentence' does not possess the clarity required of a scientific concept. Nor does the notion of a language. What are the criteria for individualizing a language? Is lowland Scots English? (Does 'bluebell' in English mean what it does in Scotland or does it mean a hyacinth as in England?) Is Etonian slang part of English? So if we use the form 'Joe desires true the sentence $S$' we are perhaps no more precise than when we implicitly refer to meanings and say 'Joe desires-true the proposition $P$.'

We can treat 'believes' in the way we treated 'desires', and for much the same reasons. Thus somebody may believe that the professor of anatomy is coming to dinner, without believing that the dean of the medical faculty is coming to dinner, not knowing that the professor of anatomy and the dean of the medical faculty are one and the same person. 'Joe believes-true "the professor of anatomy is coming to dinner"' and 'Joe believes-true "the dean of the medical faculty is coming to dinner"' makes the required distinction. Even though the professor of anatomy is identical to the dean of the medical faculty, the sentence 'The professor of anatomy is coming to dinner' is not synonymous with the sentence 'The dean of the medical faculty is coming to dinner.' Again, 'Joe believes in ghosts' and 'Joe believes in unicorns' cannot express a relation between Joe and ghosts or unicorns, because there are no ghosts or unicorns. However, there are ghost sentences and unicorn sentences, and so we can say 'Joe believes-true the sentence "ghosts exist" ' and 'Joe believes-true the sentence "unicorns exist".' Moreover, because 'ghosts exist' and 'unicorns exist' are distinct sentences, we make the distinction between believing that ghosts exist and believing that unicorns exist, even though the set of ghosts is identical with the set of unicorns, namely the empty set.

Suppose that Joe is in a pathological state in which he has forgotten his own name. Then it might be better to refer to predicates or properties rather than to sentences or propositions. Thus we could say 'Joe desires-true of himself the predicate ". . . possesses a unicorn" ' or 'Joe desires-true of himself the property [possesses a unicorn].' Or again, 'Joe believes-true of himself the predicate ". . . is at the Wolf's Crag" ' or 'Joe believes-true of himself the property [is at the Wolf's Crag].' (Following Quine I here use square brackets to turn a predicate into a name of a property.) There are technical reasons, connected with indexicality, that make the reference to predicates or properties rather than to sentences or propositions illuminating, but for my present purposes I shall ignore this refinement, and keep close to the term 'propositional attitude' by elucidating desires and beliefs as relations between a person and a sentence or a proposition.

We can think of these statements of relations to sentences or propositions as singling out states of mind such as desires and beliefs. We can also identify states of the mind with states of the brain. With adult humans this singling out can be done with some refinement. After all if Joe believes that he is at the Wolf's Crag he has a state of his brain that, among other things, will in normal circumstances lead him to assent to the sentence 'Joe is at the Wolf's Crag.' (If Joe had pathologically forgotten his own name we might do it more accurately by

reference not to a sentence, but to a predicate. We could say
'Joe believes-true of himself ". . . is at the Wolf's Crag".'
Note that while we may talk of sentences (in a given language)
as true or false, predicates are 'true of' or 'false of': '. . . is red'
is true of tomatoes, false of bananas.)

Here I am assuming linguistic ability. What of the beliefs
and desires of infants, dogs, horses, etc.? We may still identify
these with brain states related to sentences, but the identification will be a much more rough and ready one. We can
believe that the circumference of a circle is $2\pi$ times the
radius, but an infant or a dog could hardly be credited with
such a belief. It requires linguistic ability to have a belief of so
much precision. We can ascribe beliefs to infants and non-
human animals, but we must beware of implying too much. A
dog Fido may have a certain familiarity with the Wolf's Crag,
but how much are we implying when we say 'Fido believes-
true the sentence "Fido is at the Wolf's Crag"' or 'Fido
believes-true of himself ". . . is at the Wolf's Crag"'? The
mistress of a cat may say that a cat shows affection for her
when it rubs itself up against her leg, but it may be that the cat
merely enjoys the warmth of her stocking-clad legs. So there
are two dangers. The first is that of over much precision by
using semantic individuations of belief. I might believe that a
wood has 1,000 mature pine trees and distinguish this sharply
from your belief that a wood has 1,001 mature pine trees.
Fido's belief could not have this precision, because of lack of
the appropriate language. The other danger is that of
anthropomorphism, epitomized by the mistress's belief about
her cat. The danger of anthropomorphism is however not an
insuperable one, like that of attributing precise beliefs to
those who do not possess a language, in cases in which it is
only linguistic ability that allows such precision in the first
place.

Nevertheless, in a vague sort of way we may use the
language of belief and desire in order to individuate beliefs
and desires, though we must remember that the precision of
the sentences we use to individuate these vastly outruns the

precision of the identification we wish to make of state of mind (brain state). Moreover, it really goes without saying that if we were to say 'The dog believes-true the sentence "The cat is on the roof"' we are not attributing any linguistic competence to the dog. We are merely referring to the English sentence in order to pin down in a rather indefinite way a state of mind (brain state) of the dog, a state in *some* way analogous to the state of mind of a linguistically competent person who was disposed to assent to 'The cat is on the roof.' In this connection Quine has made the comparison with 'clockwise'. To say that a vortex in the plug hole of a wash basin is clockwise (when seen from above) is not to say that the existence of a vortex implies the existence of clocks.

The dodge is one of relativizing our ascriptions of belief to English sentences. This is of course arbitrary. A French speaker could relativize to a French sentence. Alternatively we could think of relativizing to a proposition, thought of to first approximation as a class of synonymous sentences. This would reduce the arbitrariness at the expense of the imprecision of the notion of synonymy. Indeed context as well as synonymy is needed. Thus 'The cat' might refer to the cat salient in my life or to the cat salient in your life. So 'The cat is on the roof' can express two different propositions. We could avoid this by referring to sentences whose truth value does not depend on context, or alternatively by saying not just 'believes-true' but 'believes-true in context C'. This leads to more scope for imprecision.

What about the more colloquial form of words 'Joe believes that . . .' and 'Joe desires that . . .'? It is tempting to believe that putting 'that' before a sentence converts that sentence into the name of a proposition. Donald Davidson has argued powerfully that this is not the right way of looking at the matter. Instead of 'Joe believes (that the cat is on the roof)' it is more nearly correct to think of the brackets shifted: 'Joe believes that – the cat is on the roof.' More accurately it is 'Joe believes that' where 'that' is a demonstrative: it refers to an utterance of 'The cat is on the roof' or to some utterance which is a 'samesayer' of it (expresses the same proposition). With this way of looking at the matter 'believes' and 'desires' work like our previous 'believes-true' and 'desires-true', and what comes after the 'that' is not really part of the sentence but is merely exhibited as what the 'that' refers to. Davidson refers to well-known philological evidence that 'that' clauses in English arose in this very way – people would just say 'Joe believes that' or 'Joe denies that' (or rather their equivalents in old English). (Davidson talks about *saying* that' but the application to 'believes that' and 'desires that' is implied.)

In identifying beliefs, desires, etc. with brain states I need not imply that your belief that it is raining is very similar as a neural hook up to my belief that it is raining, or that my desire for rain is neurologically similar to your desire for rain. (Mine might be a cowardly desire that a cricket match should end in a draw, yours that the garden lawn should be watered. But even if both our desires were for lawn watering, the details of the neural hook up could be different in the two cases.) And of course the beliefs and desires of non-linguistic creatures such as cats must be very different from ours, as their brains have no language centres. This does not prevent beliefs and desires from being identified with brain states. We identify an audio amplifier with an electronic hook up, even though the circuit of one may be different from that of another. Nevertheless, we can still expect similarities at certain levels of abstraction.

The dependence of the language of belief, desire, etc., on the notion of proposition, or the notion of samesaying, or on the individuation of a language does seem to imply that common sense psychology cannot be integrated into scientific psychology. Stephen Stich and Paul and Patricia Churchland and other recent writers have come to talk of this common sense psychological language as that of 'folk psychology'. They accord folk psychology the status of a false scientific theory, like the Ptolemaic theory or the phlogiston theory.

The word 'folk' is therefore to be taken as implying some sort of disparagement. As against this we must remember that for the purposes of explaining the behaviour of humans in the sort of way that (say) Edward Gibbon did, we have nothing better. Sometimes when folk psychology leads us astray, this is not because of the use of the concepts of belief, desire and so on in themselves, but because of hasty applications of them and wrong analogies, as when Sir Walter Scott plays at ascribing plans and feelings to a spider: 'He [Sir William Ashton] felt as a spider may be supposed to do, when his whole web, the intricacies of which had been planned with so much art, is destroyed by the chance sweep of a broom' (*The Bride of Lammermoor*, chapter 14). But the Newtonian mechanics can be wrongly applied too, as when it is applied to motions with velocities comparable to that of light. This does not mean that Newtonian mechanics is not approximately true in correct applications of it. For example, it is indispensable for calculating the nautical almanac, which would be in practice impossible using Einstein's general theory of relativity. We may suppose therefore that the generalizations of folk psychology are approximately or for the most part true. How closely the neurological states that we may suppose to be identified in our talk of beliefs, desires and so on correspond to the real things is still a matter of controversy. I find it hard to believe that in uncontroversial cases our talk of belief and desire does not correspond pretty closely to real neurological states. The predictive usefulness of folk psychology is too great for us easily to suppose that it is wildly out of touch with reality, even though we may sometimes go wrong with it. There is a method, defined by F. P. Ramsey and refined by more recent decision theory, that quantifies beliefs and desires in terms of betting quotients. An assumption of probabilistic rationality is made here, and moreover the method can be applied only in stylized situations. Nevertheless, as an idealization it may be no worse than idealizations that are needed in applying physical theory to practical situations.

In discussing psychology I have not considered the apparently mysterious phenomenon of consciousness. This has seemed to many to be incompatible with a physicalist metaphysics of mind. I shall consider this matter in the next chapter.

SUGGESTIONS FOR FURTHER READING AND
BIBLIOGRAPHICAL REFERENCES

An introduction to valency theory (the theory of the chemical bond) suitable for advanced sixth form students, is G. I. Brown, *A Simple Guide to Modern Valency Theory* (London: Longman, 1959), and more advanced is J. W. Linnett, *Wave Mechanics and Valency* (London: Methuen, 1960). An introduction to the philosophy of biology is David Hull, *Philosophy of Biology* (Englewood Cliffs, NJ: Prentice-Hall, 1974), and to the philosophy of mind is Paul M. Churchland, *Matter and Consciousness: a contemporary introduction to the philosophy of mind* (Cambridge: Mass.: MIT Press, 1984). A philosophically interesting paper by the neurophysiologist G. Adrian Horridge is 'Mechanistic Teleology and Explanation in Neuroethology', *BioScience*, 27 (1977), 725–32. For the terminology of 'teleonomy' see E. Mayr, 'Teleological and Teleonomic, a New Analysis', in R. S. Cohen and M. Wartofsky (eds), *Boston Studies in the Philosophy of Science*, vol. 14 (Dordrecht: Reidel, 1974), especially p. 91. A readable, stimulating, sometimes unorthodox elementary introduction to the study of human evolution is Mary Maxwell, *Human Evolution: a philosophical anthropology* (London: Croom Helm, 1984). On the question of folk versus scientific psychology, M. Devitt and K. Sterelny, *Language and Reality* (Cambridge, Mass.: MIT Press, 1987), chapter 15 'Rational Psychology' is illuminating. For an account and development of F. P. Ramsey's method of quantifying beliefs and desires see Richard Jeffrey, *The Logic of Decision*, 2nd edn (Chicago: University of Chicago Press, 1983), chapter 3, and Michael D. Resnik, *Choices: an introduction to decision theory* (Minneapolis: University of Minnesota Press, 1987), pp. 69ff. An amusing account of Philip Gosse's *Omphalos* will be found in Martin Gardner, *Fads and Fallacies in the Name of Science*, 2nd edn (New York: Dover, 1957), chapter 11.

For philological evidence that the word 'that' in indirect speech clauses was once a demonstrative, see C. T. Onions, *An Advanced English Syntax* (London: Routledge & Kegan Paul, 1965), pp. 153–7.

Other references are as follows: Gerald Feinberg, 'Physics and the Thales Problem', *Journal of Philosophy*, 63 (1966), 5–17; J. A. Ratcliffe, *The Physical Principles of Wireless* (London: Methuen, 1959, 9th edn revised 1952); Michael Ruse, *Philosophy of Biology* (London: Hutchinson, 1973); G. Ledyard Stebbins, *Processes of Organic Evolution*, 2nd edn (Englewood Cliffs, NJ: Prentice-hall, 1971); Gilbert Harman, 'The Inference to the Best Explanation', *Philosophical Review*, 74 (1965), 88–95; Patricia Smith Churchland, *Neurophilosophy* (Cambridge, Mass.: MIT Press, 1986); Stephen P. Stich, *From Folk Psychology to Cognitive Science: the case against belief* (Cambridge, Mass.: MIT Press, 1983); W. V. Quine, *Word and Object* (Cambridge, Mass.: MIT Press, 1960), §44; Donald Davidson, *Inquiries into Truth and Interpretation* (Oxford: Clarendon Press, 1984), essay 7 'On Saying That'.

# 5

# Perception and Consciousness

In chapter 3 I alluded to the views of some physicists that physical objects exist only when we observe them and that the collapse of the Schrödinger wave is due to the interaction of physical reality with a conscious mind outside it. (These two views are not quite the same, but could easily be held by one and the same person.) Thus the paradoxes of modern physics may be thought to support a dualist view of the relationship between mind and body, which goes back to Descartes, or a phenomenalist view, that matter is, as J. S. Mill put it, a permanent possibility of sensation, a view which, divested of some theological prepossessions, can be traced back to Berkeley.

Descartes wanted to found science on an absolute bedrock. He thought that his own existence as a conscious mind was quite certain, but that the existence of the external world was questionable. For example, he might be in a permanent dream. (Note that the word 'dream' has to be divested of certain obvious associations: normally we think that dreams occur when a person, i.e. an animated body, is asleep, maybe twitches, has rapid eye movements, etc. A certain sort of sceptic, and perhaps Descartes himself, would presumably say that we just might have experiences *as if* we were observing twitches, rapid eye movements, etc.) Descartes did not *think* that he lacked a body or that there was no external world of warm fires, snow, mountains, stars, and so on, but only that it seemed to him to make sense to suppose this. It seemed to him that the existence of himself as a conscious mind was more certain than was the existence of the external world, since the latter could consistently be doubted and the former could not. This move goes through a philosophical quagmire. The term 'conscious being' says rather more and (also less than) 'what cannot be doubted', since it enshrines a certain metaphysical view of the mind. If one leaves the metaphysical connotations to one side, one may agree that statements of sense experience say less than statements about the external world. However, they gain this extra certainty from reduction of content. If I say that it *seems* to me that there is a banana before my eyes, this can be true even if there is no banana or if I have no eyes. A man who had lost his eyes might conceivably have an *experience* as of seeing a banana, perhaps in a hallucination or a dream.

To attain greater certainty through emasculation of content is much like betting that one of all (or almost all) the horses in a race will win: there is not much possible financial advantage in this. Having doubted the existence of the external world, and having adopted the idea that there must be a bedrock of absolute certainty if we are rationally to believe anything with even a probability, Descartes was clearly going to find it hard to get back to belief in the external world and for that matter in other minds, since we come to know of other minds by observing bodily movements and activities. Scholars of Descartes are not quite agreed on exactly what his moves to do this are, but his alleged proof seemed to go from the primary certainty of his existence via a fallacious *a priori* proof of the existence of God, and an appeal to God's veracity.

Descartes makes a further and even more questionable move. Suppose we allow him the premiss that we can consistently doubt that we have a body but not that we are conscious (have a mind). He then deduces that our mind or consciousness is a different entity from our body (or any part of it, such as our brain) or activity of our body (or brain). This is very fallacious. One might be certain that nine is the square of three but not that it is the number of the planets. Nevertheless, so far as is known at present, the square of three is the very same number as the number of the planets. Analogously, Descartes' argument does not show that the mind is a separate entity from the brain or that consciousness does not consist of brain processes. The fact that we can deny the relevant propositions without logical contradiction does not imply that they are false. We may be able *consistently to deny* that a conscious experience is a brain process, and yet the experience may *be* a brain process nevertheless. Consistency is a necessary condition of truth, but not a sufficient one. Otherwise any sort of fairy story could be true.

Descartes tried to found knowledge on a bedrock of absolute certainty. The primary certainty for Descartes was that of his own existence: 'I think, therefore I am.' This takes us away from the concerns of the present chapter, where I am concerned with his assertion that we have better knowledge of our own experiences than we have of external objects. According to Descartes' methodology, science would be like a skyscraper founded on rock bottom. I advocate a better simile, Quine's 'web of belief', and a coherence theory of warranted assertibility. I shall return to this in chapter 8.

The British empiricists, Berkeley and Hume, made awareness of sense impressions the primary bedrock. Berkeley, at least, simplified the problem by cutting out 'matter' as something that is behind the sense experiences and to which we must somehow make inferences. Physical objects, such as tables or cherries, were according to Berkeley just 'congeries of ideas', an idea in Berkeley's sense being much the same as what recent philosophers have referred to as a 'sense datum', or else a mental image, which Berkeley thought of as a copy of a sense datum or a complex of such copies. The word 'sense datum' will come in handy in what follows and it can be introduced as follows. Suppose that a circular object, such as a penny, is before your eyes, and it is tilted at an angle so that (at least according to some philosophers) there is an elliptical brown something or other in your visual field. (We should be suspicious of the term 'visual field' too, but I shall let it pass for the moment, since its use is part and parcel of the sense datum philosophy.) Or, to use an example of H. H. Price's, consider an occasion on which he seems to see a tomato. Perhaps he is mistaken. He might be seeing a waxen and cleverly painted imitation of a tomato. Or he might be having a hallucination. There is, says Price, one thing that he cannot doubt: he cannot doubt that there is a red bulgy patch of colour in his visual field standing out from a background of other patches of colour. Such a deliverance of immediate experience he calls a sense datum.

The trick is that the sense datum theorist makes us go from 'It seems to me that I really see a tomato' to 'I really sense a tomato-ish sense datum.' 'Sensing' is Price's proposed word for the sort of internal seeing whose existence he is trying to make us accept. One part of the concept of a sense datum thus introduced is that it makes no sense to talk of an unsensed sense datum. In analogous ways the sense datum theorist introduces auditory, tactual, somatic and perhaps kinaesthetic sense data.

Let us interpret Berkeley, therefore, as using the word 'idea' to cover 'sense datum', in the sense introduced by Price, and also images, which are to be thought of as like sense data, but which occur in a less regular way than sense data and can often be conjured up at will.

Having introduced the notion of a sense datum, I can now introduce the philosophical doctrine of phenomenalism, according to which the physical world consists of actual and possible sense data, or better, that statements about the common sense physical world consist roughly of categorical and hypothetical statements about sense data. (Philosophically minded physicists in the tradition of Mach may say this also about the theoretical entities of science.)

In his *Principles of Human Knowledge*, part I, §3, Berkeley says: 'The table I write on, I say, exists, *i.e.* I see and feel it, and if I were out of my study I should say it existed, meaning thereby that if I was in my study I might perceive it, or that some other spirit actually does perceive it.' It was noted in chapter 3 that Berkeley wanted to say that the tree in the quad exists even when no sentient being is about in the quad. He thought that the tree was a congeries of ideas (sense data) but that it existed when unperceived by humans or other finite beings because it was perceived by God (consisted of God's sense data). We may say that according to Berkeley the tree does not exist unperceived, but that does not matter because even if we do not perceive it, God always does. Berkeley even took this as a proof of the existence of God, but it is circular, needing the premiss that objects exist when not perceived by finite beings, this premiss itself being justified by the existence of God.

## PHENOMENALISM

However, there is another way suggested in the quoted passage from Berkeley whereby he could defend the position that the tree in the quad exists even when unperceived. About the table in his study he says '. . . if I was in my study I might perceive it.' If we gloss 'might' here as 'would' (which seems to fit the context better) we have in a nutshell the doctrine of phenomenalism. According to the phenomenalist the tree in the quad can exist unperceived in the sense that certain hypothetical propositions are true: crudely that if some quad-ish sense data were being had certain tree-ish sense data would be had. (The inevitable horrible English prose of the last sentence suggests something wrong with the theory, but I am doing my best.) Or as J. S. Mill put it, 'matter is a permanent possibility of sensation.'

If one could believe this, one would not be so impressed by the vast astronomical spaces, which (as was noted in chapter 1) so frightened Pascal. Thus F. P. Ramsey, whose death before his twenty-seventh birthday was such a loss to philosophy, was a philosopher who would have fallen on the 'tough' side of William James's classification of philosophers as tough or tender minded. Nevertheless he remarked:

> I don't feel the least humble before the vastness of the heavens. . . . My picture of the world is drawn in perspective, and not like a model to scale. The foreground is occupied by human beings and the stars are all as small as threepenny bits. I don't really believe in astronomy, except as a complicated description of part of the course of human and possibly animal sensation.

It is not clear how literally to take the final sentence here. Ramsey was writing these words as part of a paper for a Cambridge discussion society and not as a piece of technical philosophy. He may merely have been saying that if we are to enjoy life we should see the world in perspective. (In contrast to this, my own view is that in metaphysics we should try to get away from particular perspectives and, in Spinoza's words, try to see the world *sub specie aeternitatis*, and that this may sometimes be beneficial for our everyday emotional life.) Nevertheless, the quotation from Ramsey is a good evocation of a certain emotional appeal that phenomenalism has for many people. Of course emotional appeal need not correlate with truth.

We have seen that phenomenalism (or something like it) comes naturally to certain physicists, from Mach to those worried about the paradoxes of quantum mechanics. From the perspective of biology phenomenalism looks, at least *prima facie*, all wrong. It seems in a way to put men and other animals inside sensation, whereas the biologist surely sees sensation as inside the animal. Moreover phenomenalism, and Berkeley's philosophy too, derives from Descartes' introspective foundationalism. If we look at perception biologically it is the acquisition of reliable beliefs by means of the senses. The reliability of perception can be given an explanation in terms of evolution by natural selection. Science gets its relative certainty from being a web of belief, in which the strands hang together. These strands will include connections to sense experience, and sense experience should of course be given its due weight, though not regarded as an impeccable source of knowledge. (If I were to perceive an alleged miracle I would suspect a conjuring trick.)

Of course the phenomenalist would say that the scientific story about human evolution, transmission of information by light rays, and neural information processing in the brain, is itself in principle translatable into hypothetical statements about sense data. Indeed the phenomenalist might say that he cannot *understand* the talk of light rays, neurons, brains, and so on *unless* it is given a phenomenalist interpretation. Thus in his well-known article 'Phenomenalism' Ayer says that once we have agreed to use the sense datum terminology we avoid the 'iron curtain theory of perception': the idea is that unless phenomenalism were true physical objects would be un-known to us because they would be barred from our perception by a wall of sense data, the things that we really observe. If this is the case, then perhaps the mistake was in agreeing to use the sense datum language at all. (Ayer was at this time at least quite favourable to phenomenalism.)

Though I shall later argue against the concrete reality of sense data, for the present I shall draw a different moral from Ayer's remark. The idea that sense data could form an iron curtain between us and physical reality (unless this is phenomenalistically understood) comes from the Cartesian notion that there must be some bedrock for our knowledge. It also comes from the idea that meaning can be given to words only by directly and individually relating them to sense experience, i.e. to sense data. However, meaning cannot be specified in this individualistic manner. Meaning is holistic. For example, a physicist can introduce the word 'neutrino' by fitting sentences containing the word 'neutrino' into our web of belief, and the word gets its meaning from the way sentences containing it fit into the web. The fact that explicit definitions are often attempted does not refute the holistic view: such definitions are usually lame, and can be ignored on future occasions. (Whoever cares at all about the original definition of an atom as an indivisible particle?)

The 'iron curtain' does not exist, since material objects could be postulated to give a simple explanation of the irregular and largely anomalous sequences of our sense data, in the same way as that in which the concepts of theoretical entities of physics are introduced in order to give a simple explanation of the irregular and largely anomalous sequence of events on the physical object level. Here I am of course trying to meet the phenomenalist on his or her own ground. In fact we do not get to the existence of physical objects by piercing a sensory iron curtain. The child learns physical object words such as 'chair' and 'tree' *first*. The idea of 'sense datum' derives from that of 'looks to me': to say 'I sense a tree-ish sense datum' is to say 'It looks to me that there is a tree.' Now 'looks to me' is closely related to 'seems'. The notion of seeming to see is clearly more sophisticated than that of seeing, and the former must be learned subsequently to the latter. So there is a good sense in which one should be more certain that there are physical objects than that there are sense data, since the concept of 'sense datum' may turn out on further analysis to be a philosophically questionable one.

However, let us provisionally grant the phenomenalist his or her sense datum language and his subjectivist epistem-ological method. Even so, we shall see that the position is not an easy one to defend.

(1) Consider the statement 'If I were having quad-ish sense data I would be having tree-ish sense data.' We may ask what the word 'I' is supposed to stand for here. If the word refers to me as a physical object or an animated body, the statement has not managed to give an account of physical objects solely in terms of sense data. Thus the word 'I' has to be understood, as Berkeley understood it, as referring to a spirit, or else it has to be eliminated entirely.

In the former case the pressure would be to give a phenomenalist account of spirits too. Berkeley toyed with this idea in his *Commonplace Book*, when he asked whether the self was a congeries of perceptions. As a bishop he could hardly pursue this line of thought, which was left to Hume to explore. In the latter case we should have to say something like 'If quad-ish sense data were had then tree-ish sense data would be had', or perhaps 'If there were quad-ish sense data they would surround tree-ish sense data', since the previous formulation invites the question 'Had by what?' Waiving this last point, we can also notice that 'If quad-ish sense data were had then tree-ish sense data would be had' also does not say enough. Quad-ish sense data could be had if one were in an imitation environment, analogous to that of an aircraft pilot's training simulator, and not in the quad at all, or if one were in some other similar looking quad. This sort of difficulty could be partially overcome by incorporating further hypothetical propositions which would tell us about the sense data one would have if one were to walk with eyes open from the quad to the High Street, for example. (We can suppose that the High Street is where we are standing when we make the statement about the tree in the quad.) If enough of this sort of thing were done this might individuate the quad sufficiently, and distinguish it from simulations. But then, as H. H. Price pointed out, this walk to the High Street, or whatever, would have to be a real one and not a matter of dreams or hallucinations. Yet more hypotheticals would be needed. It is hard to see how the process could ever stop.

(2) The hypotheticals would have to be strong or contrary to fact ones. That is, 'If I were having quad-ish sense data I would be having tree-ish sense data' could not have the sense of 'If . . . then . . .' in classical logic, which is that exemplified by 'Either I was not having quad-ish sense data or I was having tree-ish sense data.' The latter statement would be trivially true if there were no quad-ish sense data at all (no one was about in the quad). The strong conditionals would need to be backed up by categorical propositions, e.g. 'There is a tree in the quad', but this would bring us back to the

physical object language that the phenomenalist wants to eliminate. Perhaps the strong conditionals would have to be backed up by laws of nature about sense data. Unfortunately there do not seem to be any laws of nature about sense data. As H. H. Price remarked, every drowsy nod would falsify some such law. Indeed in the last chapter we saw that laws of nature do not relate even to common sense physical objects but to the hypothesized entities of physical science.

(3) The very notion of a sense datum, at least as this is conceived by the phenomenalist, is suspect. (So is that of a mental image.) Do we really have sense data? Yes, in the sense that there are certain events that we call the having of sense data. No, in the sense that there is nothing in the world that is had. 'Having a sense datum' refers to an event, but the phrase is misleading.

The term 'sense datum' was introduced in such a way that we say that a person has a spotted dog sense datum (say) if and only if it looks to that person that there is a spotted dog, and whether or not there is a spotted dog in the vicinity. That is, we are referring to our inner experience by reference to what (if it were in the offing) would be a typical cause of that experience. Having a mental image of a spotted dog can be described analogously by comparing it with the having of a sense datum of a spotted dog, i.e. the having of an experience like but yet different from the experience of having a spotted dog experience, in ways that we can immediately recognize and indeed describe in neutral language. The differences are in fact due to the having of sense data being normally (except in the case of hallucinations) externally caused, though not necessarily by their ostensible objects, whereas the havings of mental images are internally, and sometimes voluntarily caused.

Thus I hold that sense data and mental images are not part of the furniture of the world, though havings of sense data and havings of mental images are. In some respects the analogy of

'Alan Border plays an off drive' may help. 'Plays' here should not be construed as a binary predicate true of the ordered pair of Border and an off drive. 'Alan Border plays an off drive' is simply equivalent to 'Alan Border off drives.' The semantics of even this is not easy. 'Off' here might be taken as a predicate operator, but there are metaphysical difficulties, into which I shall not go, connected with predicate operators. (The difficulties have to do with ontological commitment to possible worlds other than the actual world.) Another way would be to follow Donald Davidson's semantics for adverbs, and construe 'Alan Border off drives' as 'There is a driving by Alan Border to the off side of the wicket.' Davidson can easily explain why we can deduce 'Alan Border drives' from 'Alan Border off drives' and both from 'Alan Border gracefully off drives.' It is just that if $e$ is the event of Border's off drive, '$F$' means 'drives', '$G$' means 'to the off' and '$H$' means 'is graceful', '$Fe$' follows from '$Fe$ and $Ge$' and both of these follow from '$Fe$ and $Ge$ and $He$'. Davidson treats events as a primitive ontological category, and holds that they are individuated by their causal relations to one another. But does it make no sense to talk of uncaused and uncausing events? Anyway I'm not too keen on causality in my metaphysics, or on events as a separate ontological category. It is better to treat events as ordered pairs of (1) temporal stages of objects and (2) certain classes. Let us make use of Donald Davidson's example of a ball that is heating up and rotating. The heating up stage of the ball is the same temporal stage as the rotating stage, but the class of heating up stages of objects and the class of rotating stages of objects are different, and enable us to distinguish the event of the ball heating up as a different event from the event of the ball rotating.

Well, perhaps this shows how to avoid an ontology of off drives, square cuts, drop kicks, mashie strokes, cross court volleys and what not (to use examples from various sports) but the semantics of sense datum talk and mental image talk is not so easy, if we want to avoid an ontology of sense data and mental images, as I do. I can here make only tentative suggestions. It might be asked why this matters, since 'sense datum' is a term of art which we may not need. Nevertheless 'mental image' is not a mere term of art, and unless we wish to reject our use of it as dispensable folk psychology we need a semantics for it consistent with rejecting the idea that a mental image is a piece of the furniture of the world. If we can deal with mental images, sense data pose no additional semantic difficulty.

We return therefore to the suggestion made a page or so back. Having a sense datum of a spotted dog is having the sort of experience that typically occurs when one's eyes are open, one is in good health and a spotted dog is in front of one in good light. So far so good. The difficulty comes with sense data or mental images that cannot be associated with actual objects, because there are no such objects. Thus we seem to need a 'would be': for example, a unicorn sense datum is one that typically would occur if a unicorn were before one's eyes. Perhaps a unicorn picture or statue would also do. Still, we might describe a sense datum as of something that we have no reason to believe existed or even had been pictured. The 'would be' is therefore hard to eliminate, and yet its semantic elucidation may well commit us to possible worlds other than the actual world, a commitment I decline to make.

In the previous chapter I got over difficulties about desiring the non-existent by going metalinguistic. I individuated desires, even in the case of non-linguistic animals, by relations to English sentences. Perhaps a similar dodge will do here. Suppose that there never was, is or will be a purple griffin with yellow spots and red stripes, nor any such picture or statue. 'I have a purple griffin with yellow spots and red stripes mental image' might be rendered 'I have an inner experience corresponding by relation $R$ to the English expression "purple griffin with yellow spots and red stripes".' Then something will have to be said about the relation $R$ (or perhaps the predicate '$R$').

I shall not at this stage be able to pursue the question of whether the semantics for 'sense datum' and 'mental image' can be worked out. My motivation for wanting to work out such a semantics is that the easy semantics of treating sense data and images as ghostly picture postcards is metaphysically unpalatable. Suppose that one has a yellow with purple spots sense datum or image. Let us suppose also that there is nothing in the brain that is yellow with purple spots. (If you say that there is, I shall just elaborate my example.) So if sense data are part of the world's furniture they cannot be entities or processes in the brain. They would have to be epiphenomena that go along with brain processes by laws unknown to physics or biology, and the whole idea of such epiphenomena is hard to fit plausibly into our scientific knowledge. On the other hand, the *having* of a yellow with purple stripes sense datum or mental image could easily be accommodated. The *having* of a yellow sense datum is not itself something yellow. It is just the sort of inner going on, thought by some people to be a spiritual going on, but thought by me to be a brain process, that typically occurs when something yellow is before my eyes (or is related by *R* to the English words 'yellow surface' if the metalinguistic method a page or so back is accepted). Note that in the parenthetical expression of the previous sentence I have not *used* the word 'yellow' but merely *mentioned* it.

My main objection to sense data and mental images, if conceived as furniture of the world, is, as I have said, that they do not fit into a scientific picture of humans and higher mammals. Conscious experiences are a mystery unless we are able to identify them with brain processes. Let me return, however, to the example of the spotted dog, to show something else that would be queer about sense data and images if they were part of the furniture of the world.

Consider, then, a spotted dog (Dalmatian dog, plum pudding dog). You get just a glimpse of it. The sense datum theorist would say that you had a sense datum with black spots on it. If you just had a glimpse, did your glimpse have any determinate number of spots? It looked to you that the dog was spotted, but it did not look to you that there was any determinate number of spots. And yet the notion of a sense datum was introduced in terms of how things look (or sound, taste, etc.). This should cast doubt on whether Berkeleyan ideas or sense data or mental images could be concrete entities. No concrete entity, surely, could have black spots completely surrounded by white areas, and yet with no determinate number of such spots. (Our example is not like that of clouds in the sky, in which there may be vagueness as to what counts as a cloud. Are black clouds connected together by whispy whiteness two clouds or one?)

This, then, should shed doubt on phenomenalism. What exactly are these sense data which according to it are the stuff of the physical world? We must at least consider the various philosophical problems that are ignored by physicists who think that reducing physics to talk about sense data is either possible or useful for dealing with the paradoxes of quantum mechanics. A little later I shall want to say something about mind–matter dualism similar to what I have said about phenomenalism, namely that the philosophical problems to which it gives rise can easily be ignored by mathematical physicists. My experience of biologists is that they are not, in general, in this way prone to phenomenalism or to dualism. The difficulty of integrating such theories with evolutionary and molecular biology is surely only too obvious to them.

## MIND AND BRAIN

We need to assert, therefore, or as I contend, that physical objects belong to the furniture of this world. Where do minds fit in? The view that I have partially defended in the previous chapter is that (roughly) the mind is the brain. There I was talking of such states as beliefs and desires. Here I wish to defend the view that experiences (consciousness) are brain processes.

Here I use 'brain' in a wide sense. Alpha Centaurian brains may have a different chemistry or neuroanatomy from ours.

Intelligent robots of the future may be conscious and have experiences but their brains may consist not of grey matter but of arrays of micro-chips. Let me begin by considering human brains and human experiences, and fasten on our experience of looking at a piece of yellow wallpaper with purple stripes on it. In the previous pages I have noted that a sense datum theorist would say that we have a yellow and purple striped sense datum, and I have contended that this is misleading, because the furniture of the world does not contain sense data. Nor does it contain mental images. Now the experience we describe as having a yellow and purple striped sense datum or image is not itself something yellow and purple striped. What is yellow and purple striped is the wallpaper. So even if there is nothing yellow and purple striped in my brain, the having of a yellow and purple striped sense datum can be a brain process.

But, you may possibly object, even though there are no yellow and purple striped things in my brain, or in my experience, there is surely some felt *quale* (indefinable quality in my experience) of which I am directly aware. This indefinable, or perhaps ineffable, *quale* is supposed to be something 'emergent', irreducibly psychical and inexplicable physically. My suggestion is that in inner sense, when we seem to be aware of some such *quale*, we are aware merely of certain likenesses and unlikenesses between our inner goings on. The dualist would say that these are likenesses and unlikenesses between non-physical goings on, whereas I would say that they are likenesses and unlikenesses between physical goings on in the brain. It is not presented to us in inner sense that the processes in the brain are physical or that they are non-physical. These likenesses and unlikenesses are quite abstract, or else are in terms of neutral concepts such as 'being intermittent' or 'waxing and waning'. Thus a materialist and a psychophysical dualist are able to compare their inner experiences without taking sides on the metaphysical issue. On the metaphysical issue I make the additional assertion that experiences are physical processes in the brain. This is partly for simplicity, an application of Ockham's razor (entities are not to be multiplied beyond necessity), and partly for the related reason that the physicalist neurophysiological hypothesis fits in best with biology and other sciences.

It is true that these experiences, inner goings on, may seem to be non-physical. This seeming must be explained away if I am to apply Ockham's razor as in the previous paragraph. I can at least make a shot at such 'explaining away' by invoking an idea due to David Armstrong. This idea (formulated by Armstrong in less feminist days) is that of the 'The Headless Woman Illusion'. (Perhaps nowadays it should be 'Headless Person', though I expect that historians could assure us that, despite Mary Queen of Scots and Lady Jane Grey, decapitation has been mainly a male prerogative.) In Armstrong's example a conjuror brings about an illusion by putting a woman on the stage against a black background and with a black cloth over her head, with a strong light shone on to the woman's body and its immediate surrounds. Because of the black background and the black cloth the audience do not see the woman's head. Not seeing her head they jump to the conclusion that she has no head. Analogously, Armstrong has suggested that because we are not aware of our experiences as physical we think that they are non-physical. Not perceiving them as physical we confusedly think that we perceive them as non-physical, just as in the headless woman illusion, not perceiving the woman as having a head, the audience thinks that they perceive her as without a head. I shall make another application of Armstrong's example of the headless woman illusion later in the chapter when I come to talk of colours.

Both in that case and the present one the neutrality (as between materialism and dualism) of the relevant concepts is important. Apart from likenesses and unlikenesses in respect of neutral properties such as waxing and intermittentness, we are reporting our inner processes just as being like or unlike one another, without knowing in what respect they are like or unlike. This commits me to the view that there are objective likenesses or unlikenesses, of which we can come to know without knowing the respects in which they obtain. This does not seem to me to be an obviously absurd view. After all it would be easier to build some sort of machine that would tell you simply whether coins were of the same size than it would be to build a machine that was able to register the sizes of the coins.

Thus our ordinary talk of our visual and other experiences is neutral: a materialist would think of the likenesses and unlikenesses between them as physical and the dualist might think of them as ghostly. But because of this neutrality the materialist and the dualist have enough in common to swap introspective notes. I believe that I have support in this from analyses of our sensation talk by Wittgenstein and others who had no materialist axe to grind. I also have support from the difficulty experienced by the psychologist Tolman, who spoke of 'raw feels' and yet found difficulty in giving meaning to such talk. (This matter has been well discussed by B. A. Farrell in his paper 'Experience'.)

The argument of the headless woman illusion was designed to head off (no pun intended!) the idea that our inner experiences have some *quale* (sensed yellowness, for example) whereby we recognize them. Actually if a *quale* were a metaphysically simple property there would be a problem of how we could come to be aware of it. How do we recognize some ordinary thing, such as a banana? There is a physical and informative theoretical story about this, including a story about light waves (or photons) being reflected from the banana, being refracted through our eyes and striking our retinas, of neural events in our visual cortex and other processes in our brains, so that we come to have a belief, a brain state, manifested in various behavioural ways, that there is a banana before us. Perception is the coming to have, by means of the senses, such a belief state. But how would we come to believe that yellowness exists as a *quale*? You can't bounce photons or neural impulses off a *quale*. To believe in such *qualia* you would have to believe in a supersensible intuition of pure qualities, which would be utterly mysterious on a biological and information-theoretic understanding of human and animal perception and knowledge.

## COLOURS

If colours are not *qualia* belonging to sense data or havings of sense data, what are they? If I can say how I would answer this question about colours, then it should be obvious to the reader how I would deal with sounds, smells and other so-called 'secondary qualities'. The term 'secondary qualities' refers to a distinction that goes back to Galileo and Robert Boyle, but was well made by John Locke. Thus qualities such as shape and solidity can be defined without reference to human percipients, and were called by Locke 'primary qualities'. Secondary qualities were characterized by Locke as 'powers' in the object to cause certain experiences in human percipients in normal circumstances. Locke thought of yellowness as the power to cause yellow ideas in us, and taking his word 'idea' here to mean 'sense datum' this commits him to *qualia*, which I have given cause to reject. Note that in the last sentence I have used 'yellow' in two different senses. The first one, 'yellow' as referring to a power in the object, corresponds approximately to our ordinary sense of the word, as when we say that a lemon is yellow. The other sense, in 'yellow idea', is a philosophically suspect one. Nevertheless, there is much right in Locke's view. It brings out an anthropocentricity in our concept of colour, and also that colours have objective physical bases.

The view of colour that I propose herewith is that colours are physical states of the surface of an object, e.g. a lemon, which explain certain patterns of discriminatory behaviour in normal human beings, in normal illumination of the object (daylight). By a 'normal' human percipient I mean one who is normal with respect to colour discrimination. There is no circularity here, because such discrimination can be discerned independently of prior colour concepts. Thus if there are many pieces of wool all the same length, thickness and texture, dyed in different chemicals, but secretly tagged, and Smith can distinguish pieces (suppose that they are being continually shuffled) that Jones cannot distinguish, but not vice versa, then Smith is more nearly a normal percipient than is Jones. (We can take it that the experimenter distinguishes the pieces by the tags.)

The three-colour theory of colour perception is a first approximation to an account of the human visual system: we make the colour discriminations that we do according to the colour sensitivities (as they vary over a band of wavelengths) of three different sorts of receptors in the retina at the back of our eyes. We normally try out our colour discriminations in daylight, which depends on the physical characteristics of our Sun. The three-colour theory needs to be supplemented by other considerations: for example, perhaps by E. H. Land's theory that the colours we see depend not only on the light reflected at various wavelengths of the surface of an object but also on the statistical distribution of the sort of light reflected at different places in its surrounds. So if the colour of an object is a physical state, it is partly a state of relationship to physical states of the surrounds. This only enhances a feature of the physical states which are colours: it is that colours are complex and idiosyncratic physical states. For example, if we had two- or five-colour vision (perhaps extending into the infra-red or ultraviolet) the patterns of our discriminations would be different and so would the classifications of physical states of surfaces of objects that cause the various sorts of discrimination to occur in normal human percipients. (Note that what would count as a *normal* human percipient would be different in these cases.) Note also that the physical state that is a colour is macroscopic. Individual particles, or even atoms in molecules, do not have colours. It is large-scale statistical features that count, though these are statistical features of patterns of atoms: for example, one sort of atom will emit light of wavelengths different from those of light emitted by another sort. (The emission occurs immediately after the atoms have been excited by incident light: that is what reflection is.)

The physical properties of a surface that constitute its colour are also highly disjunctive and idiosyncratic. Let me explain. Suppose that Johnny is interested only in ships, postage stamps and numbers. Then the property of being a ship or a postage stamp or a number would be of interest to those who wish to entertain Johnny. They might discuss the *Cutty Sark* or the latest Zaïre postage stamp or Fermat's last theorem and hope to entertain Johnny. Let us call the property of being a ship or a postage stamp or a number by the abbreviation '*X*-ness'. Then '*X*-ness' is a perfectly objective property: it is not intrinsically Johnny-centred as would be the property of 'pleasing Johnny'. Nevertheless, the property is of interest only to those who wish to please Johnny. Similarly the physical states that are colours are of interest only to humans. Alpha-Centaurians who had a different type of colour vision would not be interested. Nevertheless, even though colours are not only disjunctive (as *X*-ness is) and idiosyncratic (also in the way that *X*-ness is), they are perfectly objective physical states. However, it is only because of the peculiarity of our human visual systems that we bother to single them out. It is in this extrinsic sense that colour concepts are anthropocentric. This idiosyncracy explains their causal inefficacy: the way that they do not figure in laws of nature. It is true that astronomers do talk of 'blue' and 'red' stars, meaning merely that the blue stars emit rather short wavelength light on the whole and red ones rather long wavelength light on the whole, but this is a simpler concept of colour than our normal one.

Still stars seem to us to have colours in the ordinary sense too. So do rainbows, and so do stained glass windows. In none of these cases are we concerned with the physical properties of reflecting surfaces. We need to add 'or radiating surfaces or the interiors of transmitting substances'. This makes colour concepts all the more disjunctive but gives no real trouble. In the case of rainbows it might be best to treat them as illusions: it looks as though there is an archway overhead on which spectral colours are painted. After all the sky is an illusion too: there is no blue dome above us all.

Another complication in the present account is that the concept of a normal human percipient as I have introduced it may be approximate only. Smith might make the best discriminations at the red end of the spectrum and Jones the best at the blue end. Then a syndicate composed of Smith and Jones would be more nearly a normal human percipient than either Smith or Jones separately. This complication causes no real trouble.

I have based my account on the three-colour theory as a *first approximation*. I have also said that the account needs complicating to take account of physical states not only of the seen object itself but of the surroundings. It also needs, on the physiological side, to recognize information processing behind the retina and in the visual cortex, though in fact this comes out in the wash with the account of a 'normal human percipient'. The matter of surroundings can be dealt with by reference to typical lighting conditions (daylight) as including typical statistical mixtures of reflectances of surroundings. All these can be purely physical features of the object's surfaces provided that we include among these relations to the physical features of surroundings. The eye and visual nervous system adapt well to variations, as for example between midday and afternoon. The physical condition of the surface of the object of course remains the same. All this can be accommodated within the physicalist theory.

Of course in order to talk colour language we do not need to know that the states of the object that explain the discriminations with respect to colour (*not* with respect to texture, etc.) of a normal human percipient are *physical* states. (So we could talk about colours to Aristotle or to an illiterate peasant, for example.) There is a neutrality in our ordinary language of colour, but this neutrality is compatible with physicalism. The identification of the states of an object (that are colours) with *physical* states is a contingent one. Furthermore, I must remind the reader that my physicalism is an *ontological* one, not a *translational* one. Recall chapter 4 and the fact that many biological words are learned in part ostensively. This does not mean that an organism or a constituent of an organism is not a purely physical mechanism or part of a mechanism. Similarly 'normal human percipient' is not a term of physics and yet it is needed in the account of colours as physical states. Hence I reject objections to a physicalist metaphysics of colour that are objections merely to a *translational* reduction of colour concepts.

The necessity that the physical state identified with a colour should be partly a relation to states of surroundings is clear if we consider the colour brown, which has been shown to be intimately related to yellow. If all the surroundings of a brown spot are sufficiently darker than the illuminated spot itself, the brown spot will look yellow. The spectral composition of the light from a brown object is that typically reflected from yellow objects.

A white object reflects or transmits almost all the light on it, but in a diffuse manner. A transparent object transmits the light from behind it without scattering. A grey surface reflects different wavelengths in a nearly impartial manner, similarly to a white object, and hence diffusely, but it does not reflect such a high proportion of the light. So grey can vary between light grey, near to white, and dark grey, near to black, which reflects or transmits little or no light. These facts are compatible with the view that colours are physical states that explain the discriminations with respect to colour of normal human percipients.

The ordinary three-colour theory orders colour three-dimensionally with respect to hue, saturation and brightness. These should be defined not physically but with respect to the discriminations with respect to colour of normal human percipients. They can then subsequently be contingently identified with physical properties, though among these properties we may have to include relations to statistically averaged physical properties of the surroundings. Are distant blue mountains really blue? If we like we can say 'yes' and identify the blueness with physical properties of the surfaces of the mountains (or of their vegetation) together with physical properties of the intervening atmosphere. Alternatively we could say 'no' and stipulate that our normal human percipient be placed close to the mountains thus making the blueness of distant mountains count as illusion.

Our ordinary concept of colour, I suggested, is disjunctive, idiosyncratic, perfectly objective even though extrinsically anthropocentric. It is useful to compare a colour with a power of a key to open a lock. The power depends on the geometrical shape and size of the key, and it is a power because of this shape. (This analogy was made in the seventeenth century by Robert Boyle in his *Origin of Forms and Qualities*.) The shape is only of interest to us because of the shape of the lock, and yet is a perfectly objective geometrical property. (A bunch of keys would have the disjunctive property of being able to open many locks, and the property analogous to colour would be the property of having one or other of the shapes exemplified by the keys.)

Of course our ordinary common sense concept of colour may not have any relation to physics, to our talk of atoms or surfaces, etc. That is, we could talk to Aristotelians about the yellowness of a banana: they might know nothing of modern physics but might agree with us that there was *something* about the surface of the banana that explained our classifying it with lemons and buttercups and not with tomatoes and geraniums. We have enough of a *neutral* concept of colour to get on with one another: the identification of colours with physical states describable by modern physics would be a further move. If anyone were to say that he or she was aware of the colour of a banana as not being a physical property of arrays of atoms in the surface of the banana, I would once more apply the argument of the headless woman illusion, much as I did earlier in this chapter. Not perceiving the colour to be physical gets confused with perceiving it to be non-physical.

It may be objected, as has been done by Wilfrid Sellars, that we *do* perceive colours as non-physical. What is physical in the surface of a banana, say, is a discontinuous array of atoms, of none of which can we predicate colour. On the other hand, what we perceive is a continuous colour expanse. My reply to this is that the colour is a statistical property of the array as a whole, and the perceived colour is continuous only in the sense that we cannot discriminate parts of the array in any other than a coarse way. The continuity we perceive is not continuity in anything like the mathematical sense of this word, but merely an inability to make fine discriminations. That is, if a normal human percipient in normal conditions (e.g. sunlight) cannot discriminate with respect to colour between nearby parts of the surface of the lemon, then we say that the colour is continuous. Continuity of colour is a macroscopic conception perfectly compatible with discontinuity in the small.

I have introduced the notion of a normal human percipient with respect to colour discriminations made in daylight. E. W. Averill and David R. Hilbert have each suggested that we should say that two surfaces which cannot be discriminated with respect to colour in daylight could be distinguished if one allows other tests as well, by considering the surface in other sorts of lights. This would at least reduce the disjunctiveness. However, it would lead to a much finer concept of colour than that in our common sense colour vocabulary. Hilbert has argued that colours could be identified with reflectances. Reflectance is a physical property, though a dispositional one, comparable in this respect to fragility. The concept of reflectance is concerned with the *proportion* of reflected light to incident light, at various wavelengths over a band of wavelengths. This can be described as the shape of the area under a curve. Colour can then be described in terms of the reflectances of a surface over the wavelengths to which the three sorts of colour receptors in the eye are sensitive. This dispositional property of surfaces is not a disjunctive one, but it is still idiosyncratic.

I do not think that there is any important metaphysical issue as between the account I have given and those of Averill and Hilbert. Indeed reducing the disjunctiveness just makes life *easier* for a physicalist. Averill's account of colours is too complex to summarize adequately in a short space. He regards two things as different in colour if in even non-standard lighting conditions or by non-standard observers (e.g. other animals or extra-terrestrials) they could be distinguished with respect to colour. This has some intuitive advantages, and gives us a non-anthropocentric concept of colour, though it requires us to say that yellow is not a colour but a set of colours, and this set is singled out anthropocentrically.

### BODILY SENSATIONS

Besides visual experiences, auditory experiences, and so on, which usually depend on interaction with the world outside our bodies, we have such experiences as having pains, aches, itches, glows, and so on. Our way of talking about these can mislead just as our way of talking (ostensibly) about sensations and mental images may. The sensation we are aware of is such a thing as *having* an itch, *having* a pain, and so on. To see this, consider the experience that a man with an amputated left leg may describe as having a pain in his left toe. Unfortunately he does not have a left toe. He cannot have a pain in a non-existent left toe. Nor is it plausible to say that there is a ghostly pain hovering invisibly in the air where his left toe would be (or even inside a solid object, if his stump is so placed that if he had a leg his toes would have had to be within this solid object). No, just as, so I have argued, having a yellow sense datum is in the brain and not yellow, so having a pain in the toe is a process occurring within the brain, and of course is not in the toe. Neutrally described it is an inner going on that goes along with having one's attention directed towards one's toe or with thinking of a toe even though one no longer has one. This shows also that when we talk of a pain in our non-amputated foot, it is not in the foot in the literal sense that a bit of bone or a bruise is. Indeed there is no *it* at all, but only the having-of-it, which is in the brain. However, our ordinary talk of bodily sensations is neutral: we could argue with a dualist that having a pain in the toe is not in the toe, without going on to agree or disagree that its location is in the brain or in a non-physical soul. Once more the identification of the experience with a brain process is a contingent one, the one that fits most satisfactorily with Ockham's razor and our scientific knowledge.

### TYPE AND TOKEN IDENTIFICATIONS

When I spoke of identifying experiences with brain processes I have so far ignored an important ambiguity. (1) We might hold that any particular experience is identical with some particular brain process. (2) We might hold that for any experience of a certain sort it is identical with some brain process of a correlated sort. The first view has been called a 'token–token' identity theory and the second view a 'type–type' theory. (This is in analogy to an ambiguity in the use of the word 'word' which philosophers resolve by the use of technical expressions 'type' and 'token', originally due to C. S. Peirce. Suppose I send a telegram 'love and love and love'. The telegraph clerk would charge this as a five-word telegram. In another sense there are only two words 'love' and 'and' in the telegram. In the sense in which it is a five-word telegram the word 'word' is used in the sense of 'token', and in the sense in which there are two words only, the word 'word' is used in the sense of 'type'.)

It should be clear that the theory expounded above, that experiences are in fact brain processes, uses 'experience' and 'brain process' in the type sense. If we are reporting differences or similarities between brain processes when we describe our inner experience, we imply that our experience of having a yellow sense datum on Monday is similar to that of having a yellow sense datum on Tuesday. So it would appear that a single person's brain processes are compared over time, and so there are law-like constants of his or her experiential brain processes. (Here I am talking rather far away from the cognitive level of perception: clearly a person who perceives a yellow rose on Monday will have a different *total* brain process from that which he or she has when he or she perceives a yellow plague warning on Tuesday.) As far as reports of immediate experiences are concerned we must, I suggest, hold a type–type identity theory at least as far as the type–type view applies to single-person comparisons. Perhaps the brain processes you have when you gaze at a banana are different from those I have in the same circumstances. Analogy would suggest otherwise, but the point is not crucial to me as an identity theorist or for the defence of a physicalist view of reality. Similar issues between 'token–token' and 'type–type'' identity theories arise with such states as beliefs and desires, which were discussed in chapter 4.

There is a current popular philosophy of mind called 'Functionalism' which is widely thought to have supplanted the mind–brain identity theory. (And of course other philosophies of mind, such as dualism of body and spirit.) In the form in which I know it, it began with an article by Hilary Putnam according to which our talk of the mental is abstract, like our talk of a computer programme, or more accurately, our talk of abstractly described 'machine states'. Talk of these states is mathematical and neutral between various embodiments of the machine states, e.g. whether we are talking of some computer that works mechanically with gears and cog wheels or one that works in electronic fashion. There will of course be some embodiment: indeed so far as the theory goes the embodiment could be in an arrangement of non-physical or spiritual cog wheels, though few functionalists would be interested in such a possibility. Functionalists tend to hold a token–token theory. They hold that the way physics and physiology cleave the world at its joints is not the way in which language of the mental cleaves it.

Putnam emphasized the abstractness of our mentalistic language. However well this may or may not work for states of belief and desire, it does seem inadequate for the objects of reports of immediate experience. The having of a mental image or of a pain does present itself to us as a concrete process, however abstractly 'neutral' may be our description of it.

Of course we do not know the details of our internal 'machine states': these states are picked out by the behaviour to which they typically give rise and the environmental stimuli which typically cause them. But then the identity theorist picks out mental states and processes in just the same way. (The functionalist also may include in his story the relations between mental states and processes but the identity theorist can do the same too, since he or she individuates mental processes by their similarities to one another and their differences.) I think that metaphysically speaking functionalism is usually at bottom a token–token identity theory: the doctrine is put forward as compatible with physicalism and the functionalist has the same reason to think of a functional state as being physically embodied as an identity theorist has. What the functionalist is concerned with is to emphasize differences between our *concepts* of the mental and of the physical. The identity theorist will be able to agree with this: our ordinary language concept of the mental is not a neurophysiological one. It is a 'neutral' one: not specifically physicalist but not non-physicalist either. It leaves the way open for physicalist identification. Compare a word such as 'seven'. One can use the word 'seven' in the context of 'seven angels', 'seven stones', 'seven electrons'. It can occur in a physicalist discourse without itself being specifically physical. In that sense the identity theorist could agree that our (ordinary) *concept* of the mental is not physicalist but neutral, while holding that the mental itself (processes and states) are physical.

The identity theorist could also agree with the functionalist that functionally defined mental states can be realized in different physical ways. We can expect that neurologically the experiences of pain, say, in an Alpha Centaurian space visitor would be different from ours. This may even be so between your experienced pain and mine. Even so the identity theorist might expect some relatively abstract similarities of a physical sort, just as there are in the case of an amplifier using transistors on the one hand and an amplifier using thermionic valves on the other hand. The identity theorist would however hold that type–type identifications exist at least if these are confined to the experiences of a particular person, and surely this is very plausible.

We should expect more similarity between Smith's experience of pain and Jones's than between Smith's and Jones's belief and desire states. Still less would we expect much neurological similarity between the state of a cat's brain corresponding to a belief or a desire and the state of a dog's or a human brain.

How far token–token identity theories can be extended in the type–type direction is a matter for further empirical conjecture and investigation. On the main *ontological* issues the differences between the two types of mind–brain identity theory do not seem to be crucial.

I must make some qualifications to my assertion that our ordinary mentalistic language is neutral between physicalism (mind–brain identity theory) and mind–brain dualism. The person in the street may not be as unmetaphysical as I have assumed that he or she would be. He or she may have heard theological and philosophical discourse in sermons, or even read books on philosophy, for example by Descartes or Berkeley, or ideas of this sort may have percolated down to convivial discussions at tea parties or in taverns. In this case the person in the street's concept of the mental may not be compatible with physicalism. Indeed there is no hard and fast boundary to a concept. Is it part of our concept of a whale that a whale is a mammal or is this a fact that we know about whales? The question has no answer. A physicalist who believes that his or her mental states are brain states can certainly swap talk about beliefs and desires, sense experiences and pains and itches with a Catholic priest who adheres to the metaphysics of St Thomas Aquinas or with a Presbyterian minister who believes the soul to be an independent spiritual substance. Despite this difference there is a vast core of common beliefs and assumptions. It is this core of common assumptions that is neutral, belonging both to the physicalist's and the priest's or minister's corpus of beliefs.

It is worth pointing out that this qualified reconciliation of common sense with physicalism is rejected by some philosophers such as Stephen Stich and Paul and Patricia Churchland. These hold that our ordinary mentalistic way of talking presupposes a 'folk psychology' which should be totally rejected by theoreticians in favour of a new way of talking which will come from scientific psychology. They hold that there is something wrong with our ordinary concept of consciousness, which they think does not cleave nature at the joints. They also think that when we come to attain to a philosophy of mind which is thoroughly integrated into a neuroscience of the future, the aura of something ineffable, which we feel that there is about consciousness, will disappear.

Certainly from the more reconciliationist point of view that I am advocating there is a residual difficulty about consciousness even though an ontology of *qualia* is rejected, as I have suggested that it should be. One can do a bit of hand waving and say that our awareness of the similarities and dissimilarities between those neurological processes that are our immediate experiences is a matter of some sort of internal scanning. We could build a robot that was able internally to scan its internal goings on and report on them. Of course even if there were a hierarchy of some such scanning there would be a scanning that scanned but was not scanned. Does this account of consciousness exorcise the feeling of ineffability? It is not clear that it does. In chapter 2 I rejected the idea of the flow of time, and remarked that it is easier to show the absurdity of it than it is to explain its hold on us. I did make some tentative attempt to give such an explanation. In trying to deal with our feeling of the ineffability of consciousness it is even harder to avoid a charge of hand waving. I am inclined to think, however, just as in the case of the feeling of the flow of time, the feeling of ineffability is merely a symptom of some residual philosophical confusion, for which I hope further advances in philosophical analysis (combined with neurophysiological insight) will give an explanation.

If we can get rid of the supposedly ineffable (as I have argued that we can in the case of *qualia*) then we see the world as physical, and ourselves as physico-chemical mechanisms of stupendous complexity. From the physical there may emerge higher levels of organization that will still be physical. A radio receiver is not a mere jumble of components, but if we observe the way it is put together we can explain its working in a purely physical way. In this harmless sense there are emergent properties. Nevertheless, this is not the emergence of metaphysically non-physical qualities or entities. Many discussions of so-called 'emergence' are vitiated by confusion between (a) the harmless sense of 'emergence' which is compatible with physicalism, and (b) the more questionable notion of 'emergence' which is not so compatible.

SUGGESTIONS FOR FURTHER READING AND
BIBLIOGRAPHICAL REFERENCES

For Descartes see his *Meditations* in *Descartes: Philosophical Writings*, translated by Elizabeth Anscombe and P. T. Geach (Edinburgh: Nelson, 1954). For Berkeley see his *Principles of Human Knowledge, Three Dialogues between Hylas and Philonous* and the *Commonplace Book*, in volume I of *Berkeley's Complete Works*, edited by A. C. Fraser (Oxford: Clarendon Press, 1901). Further guidance can be got from the little book *Berkeley* by J. O. Urmson in the Oxford Past Masters series (Oxford: Oxford University Press, 1982). Urmson valuably stresses Berkeley's role as a philosopher of science. For John Locke on Primary and Secondary Qualities, see his *Essay Concerning Human Understanding*, edited with introduction by J. W. Yolton (London: Dent, 1961), book II, chapter 8. For J. S. Mill on matter as 'a permanent possibility of sensation', see J. S. Mill, *Examination of Sir William Hamilton's Philosophy*, edited by J. Robson (London: Routledge & Kegan Paul, 1979). Most of this chapter is in R. J. Hirst (ed.), *Perception and the External World* (New York: Macmillan, 1965), as is much of A. J. Ayer, 'Phenomenalism', which was originally published in *Proceedings of the Aristotelian Society*, 17 (1946–7), 163–91, and reprinted in Ayer's *Philosophical Essays* (London: Macmillan, 1954). H. H. Price, *Hume's Theory of the External World* (Oxford: Clarendon Press, 1940) contains interesting criticisms of phenomenalism, and a slightly Kantian interpretation or modification of Hume, with a theory of the world as consisting of sensibilia, entities supposed to be like sense data but capable of existing unsensed. The example of the spotted dog is a variant of an example in H. H. Price's review of Ayer's *Foundations of Empirical Knowledge*, *Mind*, 50 (1941), 280–93, and discussed in Roderick Chisholm, 'The Problem of the Speckled Hen', *Mind*, 51 (1942), 368–73. Price's example is itself a variant of one given by Gilbert Ryle, on 'seeing stars' when one is hit on the head, and discussed by A. J. Ayer, *Foundations of Empirical Knowledge* (London: Macmillan, 1940). For the identity theory of mind and brain see U. T. Place, 'Is Consciousness a Brain Process?', *British Journal of Psychology*, 47 (1956), 44–50, and reprinted in V. C. Chappell (ed.), *The Philosophy of Mind* (Englewood Cliffs, NJ: Prentice-Hall, 1962); J. J. C. Smart, 'Sensations and Brain Processes', *Philosophical Review*, 68 (1959), 141–56, and reprinted (slightly revised) in V. C. Chappell (ed.), *The Philosophy of Mind*, op. cit., and in J. J. C. Smart, *Essays Metaphysical and Moral* (Oxford: Basil Blackwell, 1987); D. M. Armstrong, *A Materialist Theory of Mind* (London: Routledge & Kegan Paul, 1968) and *The Nature of Mind and Other Essays* (Brighton: Harvester Press, 1981). Armstrong's argument of the headless woman illusion is to be found on p. 51 of this latter volume. Another good defence of the identity theory may be found in David Lewis, 'An Argument for the Identity Theory', *Journal of Philosophy*, 63 (1966), 17–25, reprinted in David Lewis, *Philosophical Papers*, vol. I with additional material. For my earlier views on colours see J. J. C. Smart, *Philosophy and Scientific*

*Realism* (London: Routledge & Kegan Paul, 1963), chapter 4, and for my later views see J. J. C. Smart, 'On Some Criticisms of a Physicalist Theory of Colours', in Chung-ying Cheng (ed.), *Philosophical Aspects of the Mind–Body Problem* (Honolulu: University of Hawaii Press, 1975) and reprinted in J. J. C. Smart, *Essays Metaphysical and Moral*, op. cit. The existence of *qualia* is defended in Frank Jackson, *Perception* Cambridge: Cambridge University Press, 1977). A rather different view is given in Frank Jackson and Robert Pargetter, 'An Objectivist's Guide to Subjectivism about Colour', *Revue Internationale de Philosophie*, 41 (1987), 127–41. Against *qualia* or raw feels see B. A. Farrell, 'Experience', *Mind*, 59 (1950), 170–98, reprinted in V. C. Chappell (ed.), *The Philosophy of Mind*, op. cit. Hilary Putnam's form of functionalism is to be found in his 'Minds and Machines' first published in Sydney Hook (ed.), *The Dimensions of Mind* (New York: Collier Books, 1960), and reprinted in Hilary Putnam, *Mind, Language and Reality*, Philosophical Papers, vol. II (Cambridge: Cambridge University Press, 1975). A good reply to Putnam is in U. T. Place, 'Comments', in W. H. Capitan and D. D. Merrill (eds), *Art, Mind and Religion* (Pittsburgh: University of Pittsburgh Press, 1967). For another version of functionalism see Jerry Fodor, *Psychological Explanation* (New York: Random House, 1968). The identity theory and functionalism are discussed in Paul M. Churchland, *Matter and Consciousness: a contemporary introduction to the philosophy of mind* (Cambridge, Mass.: MIT Press, 1984), an excellent short introductory book. Paul Churchland favours an 'eliminative materialism' in which he compares folk psychology (our ordinary talk of sensations, consciousness, beliefs, desires, etc.) to an outmoded scientific theory. See also Paul Churchland, *Scientific Realism and the Plasticity of Mind* (Cambridge: Cambridge University Press, 1979). For Stephen Stich on folk psychology see bibliographical notes for chapter 4. It should be added that Hilary Putnam later changed his mind about functionalism, and has argued against his former views in his *Representation and Reality* (Cambridge, Mass.: M.I.T. Press, 1988).

Other references are as follows: F. P. Ramsey, *The Foundations of Mathematics and Other Logical Essays*, edited by R. B. Braithwaite (London: Kegan Paul, 1931), 'Epilogue'; Donald Davidson, *Essays on Actions and Events* (Oxford: Clarendon Press, 1980), pp. 178–9; J. J. C. Smart, *Essays Metaphysical and Moral*, op.

cit., p. 156 n. 5; E. W. Averill, 'Color and the Anthropocentric Problem', *Journal of Philosophy*, *82* (1985), 281–304; Wilfrid Sellars, *Science, Perception and Reality* (London: Routledge & Kegan Paul, 1963).

A most interesting and readable book about our colour concepts is Jonathan Westphal, *Colour: some philosophical problems from Wittgenstein* (Oxford: Basil Blackwell, 1987). I have learned a lot from this book and it is highly to be recommended. It contains an attack on physicalism and in particular the physicalist account of colours in Armstrong and myself. I think that the attack would certainly succeed if our view was that our colour *concepts* were concepts of physics. However, my emphasis on the notion of a normal human percipient implies that colour *concepts* (though not colours) are in part *biological*. Compare the concept of a kangaroo. This may in part be introduced ostensively, and such a definition would not be part of physics. Armstrong and I are concerned with an ontological reduction: a kangaroo, for example, is nothing more than a complicated physical mechanism. We can say this without claiming to translate sentences into (or interpret them in) the language of physics. David R. Hilbert, *Color and Color Perception: a study in anthropocentric realism* (Center for the Study of Language and Information, Stanford University, 1987) is also a particularly valuable treatment of the notion of colour. Hilbert brings out the anthropocentricity of colour concepts and his account seems to me to be at least consistent with the sort of physicalist ontology that I have been advocating. See also E. H. Land, 'The Retinex Theory of Color Vision', *Scientific American*, *237*, no. 6 (1977), 108–28.

# 6

# Free Will, Fatalism and Predestination

In this chapter I shall talk about the freedom of the will and also about fatalism, comparing it in some respects with the Calvinist theological doctrine of predestination. In earlier chapters I have suggested that there are two sorts of metaphysical illusion, our feeling that time flows and our feeling that there is something ineffable about consciousness. The illusions are caused by some sort of conceptual confusion, but it is easier to diagnose the illusion than to explain it. We also have a feeling that the will is free, that we have a *genuine* choice about our actions, a genuine choice being something bigger and deeper than an ordinary choice that can be naturalistically explained. In a genuine choice (it is supposed) we are not determined by physical causes: the universe could have gone on just as it did until the moment of our decision and yet we could have chosen otherwise. It is also supposed that this freedom of choice or decision is not a matter of acting by pure chance. Suppose that a radioactive trigger in my brain were to cause me to jump out of my window and eat a spider. I do not think that I would regard this as any exercise of freedom at all, even though the transaction was an instance of indeterminism as is implied by quantum mechanics. (Let us suppose, for definiteness, that a quantum mechanical trigger gave a probability of half that this triggered event would happen over a relevant period.) This sort of indeterminism of pure chance is evidently nothing to do with free will.

Indeed R. E. Hobart, in an influential paper, contended that, contrary to what many people think, free will depends on determinism, or an approximation to it. The leading idea is as follows. As has just been noted, pure chance or indeterminism does not seem to have anything to do with freedom of choice. For an act or a choice to be free it must come from one's character, flow from our desires and beliefs. If desires and beliefs are brain states then our choices or actions must depend on an immediately preceding neurological state. Note that only a token–token identification of mental states and brain states is needed for our present purpose. Now our present neurological states, our present desires and beliefs, depend on previous states of ourselves and of the surrounding environment with which we are interacting. Determinism implies that the present state of the universe depends on the state of the universe a million years ago (for example). If we consider an ensemble of mathematically possible models of sentences which express the laws of nature and certain general statements about the structure of space-time, then any such model that contains the state of the universe at time $t_0$ as a sub-model will contain only one sub-model that is the state of the universe at any other time $t$. However, the determinist could agree that the following hypothetical statement can be true: 'If you had had different desires you would have acted differently.' Indeed it is a feature of the criminal law that it aims to inculcate beneficial desires. Without the fear of imprisonment a potential burglar would have burgled. Thus a minimal concept of free will can be tied to the notion of threat or promise, punishment or reward. Where such threats or promises are ineffective we tend to regard a person as not responsible. We do not regard an extreme kleptomaniac, say, as responsible or having 'acted freely' if such a person would have stolen even with a policeman ostentatiously watching. The difference that we make, and that the law makes, between the kleptomaniac and the ordinary person can thus be understood even on deterministic assumptions. Indeed they cannot really be understood without *some* deterministic assumptions: why have a policeman watching if this does not help to determine a potential thief's actions?

The difference between the kleptomaniac and the ordinary thief cannot easily be elucidated as a difference in free will. Some determinists have characterized free will as follows: '*A* was free to do *X* if and only if *A* would have done *X* if *A* had chosen.' This certainly makes a difference between the burglar or the kleptomaniac on the one hand and a man sliding down an icy slope towards a precipice and with no ice axe. The man wants to halt before the precipice, but no matter what he chooses (or more realistically, what he most desires, because 'choosing' is something of a success word) the man will not stop sliding down. On the other hand, it is true that the kleptomaniac, no less than the ordinary thief, would have walked out of the shop without having stolen, if he or she had chosen. The trouble seems to be that the kleptomaniac cannot choose this way – cannot help choosing to steal. The indeterminist will reply to the determinist: 'This is where we came in – as far as the main metaphysical problem that worries me is concerned.' The indeterminist will argue that what the kleptomaniac (or anyone else for that matter) would do *if he had chosen* has nothing to do with the matter: the question is whether he could have chosen otherwise. If the person could not have chosen otherwise, then this person is not free in the metaphysical sense. The indeterminist could agree that if determinism were true it would still be useful to influence people's conduct by inventing institutions of praise and blame, reward and punishment. He or she might agree that a legal institution on these lines would be useful to society. A notion of 'responsibility' could thus be used by the determinist and indeterminist alike. If a person can be swayed by argument or by praise or blame, reward or punishment then the person will be said to be responsible for his or her actions, and if not, not. Diminished responsibility could be usefully ascribed in intermediate cases, in so far as a person could be swayed by argument or considerations of reward or punishment only to a greater or lesser extent. The indeterminist could thus prize apart our concepts of free will and responsibility, conceding that some sort of pragmatic sense could be made of the latter even if metaphysically we had no free will.

But how could we have free will if our actions were not determined by our character and the circumstances, if it were pure chance whether we committed a virtuous or vicious act? The indeterminist about free will insists that free will is not a matter of pure chance. In saying that a person who acts freely is not determined to act in this way by heredity and environment, or more precisely by a previous state of the universe together with the laws of nature, the libertarian (as it is usual to call such an indeterminist) will also deny that the person acts by pure chance. The libertarian will hold that the negation of 'being determined' is not 'pure chance' but is either acting by pure chance on the one hand or 'acting by contra-causal freedom', to use C. A. Campbell's expression, on the other hand. Campbell held that contra-causal freedom comes into play only when we act from sense of duty against our greatest desire. This happens only rarely, and so Campbell can explain our usual success in predicting people's behaviour, and in (usually) determining behaviour by threat or punishment, praise or blame. Thus Campbell can come to terms with the general predictability of human action and with David Hume's dictum that the condemned prisoner feels the impossibility of prevailing against the hard heart of his gaoler as much as against the stone walls of his cell.

It is usually assumed that classical physics is deterministic. The matter turns out to be a difficult one. See the reference to John Earman in the bibliography at the end of the chapter. However, I think that we can say at least that the definition of determinism applies approximately to relatively isolated classical sub-systems but not to quantum mechanical systems, however isolated. Moreover, if by 'classical physics' we understand particle mechanics as modified by special relativity together with Maxwell's electromagnetic theory the definition of determinism that I have used does well enough. So I shall ignore these difficult extra subtleties, in the belief that they have no particular reference to the discussion of free will. (It is good at least that they should be hinted at.) We can say that the world (or an isolated sub-system of the world) is deterministic or indeterministic according as to whether we think that the true theories about the world (or an isolated sub-system of the world) are deterministic or indeterministic. Because we believe that quantum theory gives the fundamental theory of the world (excluding, perhaps, gravitational phenomena) we believe that the universe is indeterministic. Nevertheless on the macroscopic level quantum mechanics predicts deterministic behaviour with a probability so near to one that in considering human behaviour we can probably assume that our brains are deterministic mechanisms. A single neuron, or even a single protein molecule, is macroscopic by quantum mechanical standards. It is not inconceivable that there are quantum mechanical triggers in our brains, but it is unlikely, and unimportant anyway as this would introduce a mere element of uncertainty into overwhelmingly deterministic behaviour. Or to be fair to Campbell, this would be so unless there was another sort of indeterminism besides pure chance: acting from contra-causal freedom.

Unfortunately I can make no sense of this concept of contra-causal freedom. One idea might be that the mind is immaterial and gives some sort of minute kick to a triggering device in the brain. This however merely pushes the problem back only to recur again. Does the immaterial mind give this push by pure chance or is it determined by its own character together with psychical laws? Neither alternative seems any more palatable than the original ones.

Another idea might be that though acts from contra-causal freedom are not caused, they are determined by reasons. There are several objections that can be raised to this idea. In the first place, 'reasons' may mean our desires or attitudes. But desires and attitudes figure in the common sense causal explanation of actions. Indeed it would seem obvious to some of us that we could not act against our greatest desire. We could act against the greatest of our desires other than our sense of duty, but this 'sense of duty' is just a desire to do what one ought, and would figure in a causal explanation. There would be nothing 'contra-causal' here. In the second place, 'reasons' may mean something like 'propositions'. In this case reasons cannot be causes, but nor could they be contra-causal either. They are outside the causal story altogether. They are not in time or space. So how could they influence something so that it happens at a particular time? Why that time rather than some other time? Perhaps some answer to this question might be concocted, but the problem remains as to how reasons could be contra-causal agents as opposed to causal ones. I conclude that there is no way in which I can attach meaning to the notion of 'contra-causal freedom'.

Campbell thinks that introspection at the time of moral choice can give meaning to the notion of contra-causal freedom. This is in conflict with the best contemporary theories of meaning. A meaning is not an image or feeling in the mind. Suppose that we do have a certain feeling, perhaps of muscle tenseness, gritting of teeth or whatever, at the moment of moral choice. This has no intimate connection with a notion like 'contra-causal'. Perhaps what we interpret is not a feeling but a saying to ourselves 'I can do this and I can do that.' This will not help if no meaning has *already* been given to this supposed contra-causal sense of 'can'.

To make this clear I need to make a few remarks about the words 'can' and 'is possible'. Possibility is a matter of consistency with contextually agreed background assumptions. Thus I might say that I can go out to dinner with you next Thursday. I am saying that the proposition that I go to dinner with you next Thursday is consistent with propositions about my state of health, my transport facilities, my honouring certain engagements in my diary, and so on. Suppose that I break my leg on the Wednesday. Well, I wasn't saying that my going out to dinner with you was consistent with a set of propositions that included the proposition that I break my leg on Wednesday.

Metaphysically an important sense of 'can' is that of consistency with background assumptions about what the laws of nature are. We often say that something could have happened if it would have happened if the laws of nature had been the same but the initial conditions had been appropriately different. And to say that $p$ would have been the case if $q$ had been the case is just to say that $p$ follows logically from the conjunction of $q$ together with certain appropriate and contextually agreed background assumptions.

What is odd about the libertarian's notion of contra-causal freedom is that the libertarian wants to say that we cannot do an act $A$ if $A$ is inconsistent with the conjunction of the laws of nature *and* the initial conditions. This certainly is to make contra-causal freedom inconsistent with determinism. (Moreover, as I have suggested, if there is also a bit of pure chance in the offing, this doesn't make for free will.) Normally we use 'can' in a less demanding way. This is the sense in which a china plate could have broken (when you had dropped it) whereas an aluminium plate could not have. If the initial conditions had been slightly different in a certain way the china plate would have broken, but however you dropped the aluminium plate it would not have broken.

If we use 'can' in the extreme way demanded by the libertarian then I think we have to concede that we do not have free will. This conclusion is less worrying if we remember that in a more relaxed sense of 'can' it is often the case that we can do something $A$ and that we also can do something incompatible with $A$. We can make a lot of the usual distinctions about moral responsibility. We can treat someone as responsible if praise or blame, punishment or reward, or just the giving of reasons would have altered his or her behaviour. The determinist's notion of free will is akin to this notion of responsibility.

This is the notion of free will that R. E. Hobart claimed was compatible with determinism, and indeed required the truth of determinism or an approximation to it. Now since the notion of free will is not a precise one we can go in two directions. We can take the reconciliationist position of Hobart and argue that free will is perfectly compatible with determinism. (And also that any indeterminism in the world does not increase our freedom but in fact detracts from it. Doing something by pure chance is no exercise of free will, nor of rationality.) However, there are pressures to go in the other direction, and to say that we do not have free will, because libertarianism is unintelligible and because the compatibilist attempt at reconciliation (such as Hobart's) is unsatisfactory.

One reason why some of us may think that this sort of attempt at reconciliation is unsatisfactory is as follows. Consider the following piece of science fiction. An eminent female poet is captured by a mad scientist, who has a device for rewiring a living brain by altering synaptic connections, and also for changing the brain's memory store. The mad scientist does this in such a way that the poet's memories of writing poetry, studying literature and prosody, and so on are replaced by pseudo-memories of learning the theory of structures, the design of bridges, about the strength of materials, and so on. These changes also alter the person's desires. No longer does she wish to write poetry or read Shakespeare and Wordsworth: she now prefers to read the biographies of the two Brunels, to build suspension bridges, tunnel through mountains, make routes for high speed trains, and so on. She is at least as happy in her new life as she was in her now forgotten poetic past. She fulfils all the criteria the compatibilist philosophers demand for free will. She is amenable to praise and blame, threats and promises of reward, as well as to reasoned argument. Her choices are her own: what she does is caused by her own acts of choice, and often stems from her own extended deliberations. Hobart would have had to say that the one-time poet but present engineer was perfectly possessed of free will. Other philosophers would be likely to demur. The engineer's actions were determined in part by her character, but her character was determined for her by the mad scientist.

This piece of science fiction is of course put forward purely as a philosopher's thought experiment. The case is probably technologically impossible, even with unimagined advances of technology in the future. Nevertheless, analogous things occur. A person's character may be changed by a piece of shrapnel or by a brain tumour or by the irreversible effect of certain drugs. So the science fiction example is largely rhetorical, to point up in stark form what is less easily visible when we look at certain actual phenomena. We sometimes observe big personality changes in people as a result of brain lesions. It is generally thought that a person's free will has been impaired. Yet if determinism is true or approximately true what is the metaphysically important difference, it may be asked, between lesions due to accident or disease, and misconnections in the brain of a person which lead him or her to perform criminal acts? Are not these due to heredity and environment?

These considerations may lead us to reject compatibilism. A man who commits a murder because of a lesion in his brain, has none the less presumably acted from choice, possibly from deliberation, and his action proceeds from his desires. Admittedly it may be that he would not have had these desires but for the lesion, but that does not affect the matter. We are not responsible for our heredity any more than this man is responsible for his lesion.

If after an autopsy a lesion were found in the brain of an executed criminal, even staunch advocates of capital punishment would feel uneasy. The law would suppose that the existence of a brain lesion gave a case for admitting diminished responsibility for a crime. Is the law therefore an ass? This is not necessarily so. On deterministic assumptions threat of punishment (ascription of responsibility) encourages potential criminals not only to avoid crime but even to act in such ways as to improve their own characters. It might reduce such a commitment to improving one's character if there were cases of persons who cultivated moral desires up to the time of a lesion and were then punished for acts they had done after getting the lesion.

A libertarian might therefore allow that the determinist might give some utilitarian grounds for the way the law and moral custom commonly work in making ascriptions of full or diminished responsibility as the case may be. Nevertheless, he or she will still want to say that determinism is incompatible with free will in the metaphysical sense. However, I have given reasons for saying that indeterminism does not help either. I conclude that we can go two ways, either using 'free will' in the compatibilist sense, which is well enough for practical purposes, or else going the other way and denying that we have free will at all. The compatibilist can give the plain man what he needs for using 'free will' in contexts of utilitarian justification of ascribing responsibility, meting out punishment, and so on. Alternatively one might drive a wedge between the notion of responsibility and that of free will and might deny that we have free will at all. In the compatibilist sense an electronic machine of the future could conceivably have free will. In the libertarian sense neither we nor anything else could.

## FATALISM

I want now to say a little about fatalism, a view with which determinism is sometimes confused. You can be a fatalist without being a determinist. You can even be a libertarian and also be a fatalist. A compatibilist is not necessarily a determinist. A compatibilist can agree with modern physics that the universe is indeterministic, even though near enough deterministic so far as macroscopic phenomena are concerned. A compatibilist merely says '*If* determinism is true we could still have free will, and indeed at least an approximation to determinism is necessary for free will.' The compatibilist, in accepting indeterminism, rejects libertarianism as unintelligible. But like the determinist and the libertarian the compatibilist might nevertheless be a fatalist. Admittely the compatibilist may also reject the arguments for fatalism.

The force of fatalism may be easily felt if we consider the Minkowski space-time view of the world, a view that I advocated in chapter 2. The appropriate way of talking in metaphysics and theoretical physics, I suggested, was a tenseless one. Events in space-time *exist* (tenseless present). If we want to go tensed we can use the tenseless present with an indexical 'here-now'. Past events *exist* earlier than here-now. Future events *exist* later than here-now. Events outside the light cone whose vertex is 'here-now' *exist* neither absolutely earlier nor later than here-now, though they *exist* earlier or later or simultaneously with reference to a chosen inertial set of axes. So if at some time $t_0$ a person *is* contemplating his or her future, there *is* that future up ahead of $t_0$ in Minkowski space-time. (Note that I have italicized 'is' in the last sentence, to indicate tenselessness.) So it is easy to get the idea that the future is 'fixed' (in the way that the past is supposed to be). If the event of your falling off a mountain *is* up there in Minkowski space-time in the 1990 segment of your world line, then you are jolly well going to fall off the mountain in 1990.

You might find this thought disturbing. But ought you? If the event of your falling off a mountain *is* up there in Minkowski space-time in the 1990 segment of your world line then you are jolly well going to fall off the mountain in 1990. Isn't this to assert the merest tautology, near enough 'If $p$ then $p$'?

It would be different if you knew more than this. For you to know that if you fall off a mountain in 1990 then you fall off a mountain in 1990 is to know no more than that your utterance of the sentence 'I fall off a mountain in 1990' has a truth value. But what if you knew not only the tautology 'If $p$ then $p$' but also $p$ itself, i.e. that you fall off a mountain in 1990? *Then* the cat would be among the pigeons. Would you go to live in Holland or in the Fens where there are no contour lines to speak of on the maps? Perhaps you never moved from there until 1992 (to be on the safe side). So you don't fall off a mountain in 1990. This would show that you did not after all know that you would fall off the mountain in 1990. Perhaps you believed on the best scientific evidence, based on a revolutionary new theory of space-time, and a scientifically induced vision of a dated report in the London *Times* of 1 July 1990 describing your mountaineering accident. (The story here is closely modelled on parts of John Buchan's novel *The Gap in the Curtain*.)

The important thing (for present purposes) of my supposition that you *knew* is that it is part of the meaning of the word 'know' that if you know that *p* then '*p*' is true. However good your reasons for believing that *p*, if it turns out that not *p*, then you must withdraw your claim that you knew that *p*. Now your name might be 'Adolphus McGillicuddy Gartcosh', and your vision of the future might have been of a *Times* report, dated 1 July 1990, of a person of that very unusual name having fallen off a mountain the previous day.

You would be irrational in (a) saying that you knew that you, Adolphus McGillicuddy Gartcosh, *falls* (tenseless) off a mountain of 1 July 1990, *and* (b) intending to spend all of 1990 in Holland. The going to live in Holland would have no causal connection with the reliability or otherwise of your vision. If the vision was illusory, or if it was of a misreport, or a report of a namesake's death (unlikely though that would be), then why go to live in Holland? Why not enjoy, with good fortune, the pleasures of mountaineering?

Suppose, then, that you do continue mountaineering in 1990 and duly fall off the mountain on 1 July. Your wife might think 'Adolphus should have gone to live in Holland.' In the light of my remarks in the previous paragraph, this might be considered to be an irrational response.

Richard Taylor in his *Metaphysics* (second edition especially) has made it clear that the fatalist worry depends only on the tenseless *truth* of propositions about the future. The story about knowledge comes in only because knowledge that '*p*' implies the *truth* of '*p*'. The idea is that if '*p*' is true, then what '*p*' says tenselessly will occur is unavoidable.

Let us examine this suggestion. First of all, the fatalist worry has nothing to do with the question of determinism or indeterminism. To say that determinism is true is to say that events are connected with earlier states of the universe in a certain law-like way. Even if these law-like connections are absent, there is still the fact of the *truth* of the proposition about the future to worry us. Now if we accept the law of excluded middle we must hold that either '*p*' is true or 'not-*p*' is true. So, we may be tempted to say that either '*p*' is fated to occur or 'not-*p*' is, and that whichever it is is unavoidable. Or so Taylor has argued.

Taylor thus equates fate with a certain sort of unavoidability. It has to be this to be interesting or worrying, because who could be either worried or reassured by 'What will be will be' if all this comes to is the conjunction of two tautologies (and so itself also a tautology), 'if *p* then *p* and if not-*p* then not-*p*'?

Taylor disapproves of those who characterize fatalism as the view that 'certain things were going to happen, *no matter what.*' To characterize fatalism in this way, he thinks, is to allow too easy a refutation of it. Yet we do come across ordinary people who engage in fatalist ways of thought of this childish description. There is the soldier who needlessly exposes himself to enemy fire, because he thinks that he will be hit if the bullet 'has his number on it' (not that bullets are inscribed with numbers anyway!) There are people who smoke tobacco and comfort themselves with the thought that either they'll get cancer or they won't, and in the former case they might as well enjoy smoking and if they won't it won't matter whether they smoke or not. Or they may refuse medicine because either they'll get better, in which case the medicine was unnecessary, or they won't get better, in which case taking the medicine was pointless. This is indeed childish reasoning, neglecting the fact that if they don't get cancer this may be because they didn't smoke, and if they get better from an illness this may be because they took the medicine. Their reasoning is obviously fallacious 'no matter what' reasoning. Taylor says that a sensible fatalist, such as himself, would not deny that if an event occurs in the future the events necessary for the occurrence of that event must occur too. (Thus in my example of the person who falls off the mountain on 1 July 1990, the person just could not have spent all of 1990 in Holland.)

Taylor's characterization of fatalism is in terms of the fact that there are true propositions about the future (whether we know them or not) and the fact that the comings to be true of these propositions are events that are unavoidable. My difficulty with Taylor's argument lies in the use of the word 'unavoidable'. I am inclined to think that though he rejects a 'no matter what' thesis he nevertheless needs a 'some matter what' thesis.

Let me explain. 'Avoidable' means 'can be avoided'. To say that an event $E$ can be avoided is to say that the non-occurrence of $E$ is consistent with certain contextually agreed background assumptions. Similarly, to say 'If I had done $X$ then $Y$ would not have occurred' is to say that 'I did $X$ and $Y$ did not occur' *follows* from certain contextually agreed background assumptions. For example, a person could say that if he had taken the anti-malarial pill mepacrine then he would not have got malaria, even though bitten by female anopheles mosquitos carrying the malaria parasite. The background assumptions will notably contain the proposition 'No persons who take mepacrine regularly get malaria.' Some of the background assumptions will be contrary to fact. One will be that the person in question did not get malaria. In asserting contrary to fact conditionals we are making assumptions according to which the course of the world is very like its actual course but with slight differences. How to make the slight changes so that the whole story remains consistent is a delicate matter which would need to be taken into account in a formal treatment, but in our loose everyday discourse we tread easily enough past these pitfalls.

Now your falling off a mountain in 1990 is avoidable in the sense that if you choose to live in Holland in 1990, then, since there are no mountains in Holland, you do not fall off a mountain in 1990. Indeed falling off the mountain in 1990, even though you do climb the mountain, can be said to be avoidable if the background assumptions include the proposition that you take even more care than usual. We consider a contextually agreed story that differs from the facts, including the fact that you *do* fall off the mountain. If you *do* assume this fact then all we get is the tautology that if you fall off the mountain then you fall off the mountain. And why should that worry you? If the fatalist says that event *E* is fated and then includes in background assumptions the statement that event *E occurs* he has implicitly adopted an empty sense of 'avoidable' which should not worry us any more than 'What will be will be' should worry us. If this is fatalism it is a totally empty doctrine.

Thus though the problem posed by the fatalist argument is different from that of free will, I locate the difficulty in giving sense to it in very similar places: in the fatalist's use of 'avoidable' and in the libertarian's notion of 'contra-causal freedom'.

Some philosophers, such as A. N. Prior, have differed from the line taken in the present book in that they have taken a fundamentally tensed view of truth. Propositions about the future, such philosophers hold, are neither true nor false, though they will become true or become false. In other words, they hold that the future is indeterminate. They think that as the future becomes present and then past it changes from being indeterminate to being determinate. This is to suppose a type of change that in chapter 2 I have given reasons for rejecting. The future is perfectly determinate, up there ahead of us in Minkowski space-time. There can be indefiniteness, as with the position or momentum of a particle, on account of quantum mechanics, but this indefiniteness is no more in the future than in the past: consider the puzzle as to which slit or neither a particle goes through in a two-slit experiment in 1940 AD and in a two-slit experiment in 2000 AD. Note that before the collapse of the Schrödinger wave that gives the particle a definite position and infinitely indefinite momentum (or in another type of experiment vice versa) both the propositions 'The electron has a definite position' and 'The electron has a definite momentum' are false. Thus the indefiniteness in quantum mechanics does not imply indeterminateness or absence of truth value of propositions, or a third truth value different from 'true' and 'false'.

Thus we must say that the future is determinate, just as the present and past are. The whole universe is determinate. This is so whether it is deterministic (as used to be believed) or is indeterministic (as is at present believed). The determinateness of future events does not imply determinism. An event can be just as determinate whether its occurrence does or does not depend on the laws of nature together with some earlier state of the universe.

One good thing about thinking of the world spatio-temporally is that it gives us a strong sense of the reality of the future. (A sense that we ought to have anyway.) Because of muddled thinking a lack of feeling for the reality of the future is quite common, and I shall suggest shortly that this muddle may have dangerous practical consequences. Some philosophers have questioned not only the reality of the future but that of the past. This is because of the tendency of a certain type of philosopher to confuse a proposition with the evidence for it, or warranted belief with truth. Consider a famous statesman in pain from a serious illness. In a hundred years' time history books record the statesman's pain and positivistically minded philosophers of the next century say that talking about the pain is just a way of talking about inscriptions on paper (e.g. letters expressing his feeling of agony), tape recordings, and so on. This seems to be a mad philosophy of history. Similarly with the future. The statesman might feel very annoyed if told that positivistically minded philosophers of the last century had denied the reality of twentieth-century pains.

Of course philosophers of the last century who denied the reality of twentieth-century pains might have been denying that they were real *then*. I can agree with this if what we have here is just a slipshod way of saying that twentieth-century pains do (tenseless) not exist then (i.e. in the nineteenth century). Of course no pains could be in both centuries. (Unless perhaps long pains that overlapped the end of the nineteenth century and the beginning of the twentieth century!) Analogously one might say that a rock in Sri Lanka is not real in Iceland, but this would be a misleading way of saying that there are no rocks that are both in Sri Lanka and in Iceland.

We cannot name future events ostensively. Nevertheless, we can refer to them by description. Consider the use in the Old Testament and indeed by Jews at present of the phrase 'The Messiah', which is short (to use a quasi-logical notation) for 'The $x$ such that $x$ *is* (tenseless) the promised deliverer of the Jews'. It is true that this does not work like a name, because a description may fail to refer. A descriptive phrase is what used to be called 'an incomplete symbol'. We translate 'The Loch Ness Monster is reptilian' as follows: 'There is an $x$ such that $x$ is reptilian and for any $y$, $y$ is a monster in Loch Ness if and only if $y$ is identical with $x$.' This ensures that we are saying that there is a Loch Ness monster and only one such monster and that it is reptilian. Logicians call the '$x$' and '$y$' here 'bound variables'. Reference can be carried by such variables: indeed in W. V. Quine's canonical notation names are parsed as predicates: 'Socrates' becomes 'the Socratizer', where to Socratize is to have a snub nose, be a philosopher, or whatever. (Even if you were a benighted metaphysician who thought that Socrates had some simple ineffable essence, to Socratize would be to possess this simple ineffable essence!) Certainly we cannot name future events ostensively, as we might point to a baby and say 'Henceforth this baby shall be called "John".' However, we can refer to future events descriptively, and even in a sense name them (e.g. 'The first eclipse of the sun during the next century') and even at least purport to refer to them (that is, we succeed in referring only if there is something that answers to our description) as with 'Armageddon'. (At least I *hope* that this word fails to refer!) Bound variables can fail to convey reference only in an empty universe, and our universe is of course not empty.

Connected with the idea that the future is unreal is the idea that we can alter the future but not the past. Now certainly we can causally determine the future but not the past, because in action we are operating an information flow system whose memory base depends on the asymmetry about traces which I discussed in chapter 2. Modulo the fact that I'm not keen on the notion of 'causality' as an appropriate one for theoretical physics, I am open to ideas about backwards causality as regards elementary processes, but macroscopically there does appear to be an asymmetry in the causal grain of the universe. But to say that we can determine the future is not to say that we can change the future. Suppose that I try to change the future by lifting either my left hand or my right hand. I decide to lift my left hand. This does not change the future. Lifting my left hand was the future. The notion of changing the future is equivalent to that of changing things in the Minkowski space-time world. This involves the illegitimate notion of a hyper-time through which the four-dimensional world endures. The attempt to change the future is as foolish as the attempt to demonstrate free will by doing the opposite to what one has just done. As Hume says (*Inquiry Concerning Human Understanding*, section VIII, part I, n. 7) we feel that 'the will moves easily every way' and when we try to demonstrate free will 'We consider not that the fantastical desire of showing liberty is here the motive of our action.' (Hume means 'free will in the libertarian sense' – at bottom he is a compatibilist.) Similarly the fantastical desire of showing that we can change the future does not succeed – we merely cause the future to be what it *is* (tenseless).

The muddled idea of 'changing the future' is behind the metaphor of a book of destiny. 'The Moving Finger writes and having writ, / moves on: nor all thy Piety or Wit / Shall lure it back to cancel half a Line . . .' (Edward Fitzgerald, *The Rubáiyát of Omar Khayyám*). The question is transferred from that of whether I can change the future to whether the Moving Finger can. But if the Moving Finger writes '*p*' tomorrow then writing '*p*' *is* (tenseless) just its future. The poem suggests the irrevocableness of the past. But if talk of changing the past is absurd, so also is (I have suggested) talk of changing the future. This is consistent with the correct thought that we can cause the existence of future events. Fatalism does not imply the sort of powerlessness that goes with our ordinary notion of unavoidability. Moreover, I have suggested that if the fatalist's notion of 'unavoidable' is *not* our ordinary one it is innocuous, merely adverting to the tautology that what will be will be. Tautologies cannot be frightening: after all they say nothing.

The present book is on metaphysics, not on ethics. It is about what the universe is like, not about what we ought to do. Nevertheless, I shall suggest that a strong sense of the reality of the future is of ethical importance. If my considerations in previous pages are correct the future is more important than is the past existence of the human race. There is so much of it. If terrestrial beings do not destroy themselves there may be hundreds of millions of years of further life on earth or of expansion of life from earth to outer space. The great nations are able to destroy one another with their nuclear warheads. Politicians often say 'It has kept the peace.' Well, it has kept the world from all-out thermonuclear war for thirty or forty years. There is always nevertheless the fear of accidental war. Even if the probability of accidental war occurring in any one year may be small, over many years it can become a near certainty. Even if we could keep the peace for a thousand years, this would be a mere drop in the ocean with the hundreds of millions of years of possible further evolution that lie before us.

Unfortunately the politicians, businessmen and generals who run our affairs usually have limited mental horizons: they tend to look forward only to the next election, the next meeting of a politburo, and so on. But even if they look forward ten or a hundred years, this is miniscule when we consider the possible further evolution of the human species into higher forms of life over (say) the next 500 million years. All this might be lost as the result of nuclear destruction. A strong feeling for the reality of the future would bring about a feeling that the stakes are so high that the question of nuclear war is of quite transcendent importance.

It may be objected that politicians do care about the near future, and the metaphysical status of the near future is no different from that of the far future. They care about their future careers, for the future lives of their spouses, children, or even grandchildren. None the less, I suspect that they lack a grip on the reality of the far future and that the inconsistency of this with their concern for the near future may be part of the general metaphysical haze in which so many practical (and impractical) persons live their lives. My own feeling is that a keen sense of the reality of the future is of the first importance for making us see the desirability of long-term political concern. 'It has kept the peace' (for only thirty or forty years?) is too complacent a remark by a very long way indeed.

Some may say that a concern for the reality of the future is likely to work the other way. Some people may become quietist if they think that belief in the reality of the future is tied to fatalism. I have tried to argue that it should not be so tied. We cannot change the future but our actions are parts of the causal chains that determine what the future *is*.

Nevertheless, the contemplation of the future can give us a strange metaphysical feeling. Consider the temporal stage of the earth corresponding to 500 years hence. Will there be life on earth? Will there be a sterile environment hostile to life, as a result of thermonuclear catastrophe? Or will there, perhaps, be something at the other extreme, a civilization superior to ours, with a happy and contented world population? Or something in between? The answer to these questions lies up forward in Minkowski space-time. This may lead to quietism if we forget that if a good state of the world *does* lie up forward in Minkowski space-time this is probably because we are working towards it now.

Compare the Calvinist doctrine of predestination. The *main* idea of this comes from the doctrine of justification by grace, not by works. This is in contrast with the Arminian doctrine that salvation comes from free belief in the Gospel. According to Arminianism this belief in the Gospel would result in good works, and grace and salvation are the results of this free belief. According to Calvin such belief and good deeds are the effect of God's prior choice, not what caused God (by his foreknowledge before the world began) to elect some and reprobate others. Calvin regarded all persons as equally sinners, because of Adam's fall, and God chose some sinners for reprobation (and hell fire!) and others for his grace and thus for salvation. If it was asked why an almighty and benevolent God would choose *any* person for reprobation, Calvin replied that it was absurd of us finite minds to question or criticize the purposes of the infinite God – these purposes must remain unknown to us. To such questioners he would come out with biblical texts. Such appeal to revelation seems to be quite unphilosophical, and moreover Calvin's ability to tolerate contradictions in theology (telling us not to worry about them but to remember the finiteness of our understandering) is quite remarkable.

The ethical misuse of the doctrine of justification by grace is a major theme of James Hogg's *Memoirs and Confessions of a Justified Sinner*. Believing himself to be possessed of salvation, due to the grace of God, the main protagonist in this story committed various crimes, secure in the belief that his salvation in no way depended on works.

Powerful though Hogg's story is, its main theme seems to be contrary to the more usual psychology of most Calvinists. The Justified Sinner seems to have been a schizophrenic, and here Hogg seems to have had good psychiatric insight. Though the Calvinists denied that good works are in any way rewarded by God's grace, they naturally regarded any virtue they exhibited as a *sign* of God's grace. Thus if they did good work they would feel a glow of satisfaction, due to the strengthening of their antecedent belief that they were among the saved. Justification was not (even indirectly) by works but works could be evidence of prior justification.

The situation has some similarity with that described in Newcomb's Problem (due originally to Dr William Newcomb of the Livermore Radiation Laboratories in California, and first presented to the philosophical public in an article by Robert Nozick). You are placed in front of two boxes and given a choice either of taking the right-hand box only or of taking both boxes. You are reliably informed that a superior being from outer space has the capacity almost infallibly to predict human actions. You are also reliably informed that the being has placed $1,000 in the left-hand box and that in the right-hand box the being has placed either $1,000,000 or nothing according to the following rule. If the being predicts that you will take the right-hand box only it puts $1,000,000 in that box. If it predicts that you will take both boxes it puts nothing in the right-hand box.

Should you take the right-hand box only or should you take both boxes? There seems to be a highly attractive argument for each of these incompatible alternatives.

In the first place, you know that either there is $1,000,000 in the right-hand box or there is nothing in the right-hand box. It is part of the story that money does not mysteriously disappear from the boxes. Nothing you do will cause $1,000,000 to disappear from the right-hand box if you decide one way or the other. If you take both boxes you will get either $1,000 or $1,001,000 as against nothing or $1,000,000 if you choose only the right-hand box. So whether or not there is $1,000,000 in the right-hand box, you will do better by taking both boxes. In the technical language of decision theory this is the argument from *dominance*. In each of the two possible cases ($1,000,000 in the right-hand box and nothing in the right-hand box respectively) the choice of both boxes *dominates* the choice of the right-hand box only.

In the second place, you could argue from expected utility. The expected utility of taking the right-hand box only is $1,000,000 multiplied by the probability of there being that sum of money in the right-hand box plus zero dollars multiplied by the probability of there being zero dollars in the right-hand box. According to the story the probability of there being $1,000,000 in the right-hand box relative that you take that box only is near to one. And the probability of there being zero dollars in the right-hand box if you take the right-hand box only is near to zero. So the expected utility of taking only the right-hand box is near to $1,000,000. On the assumption that you take both boxes you have a probability of one of getting the $1,000 from the left-hand box and a probability of near to zero of getting $1,000,000 from the right-hand box. So if you take both boxes the expected utility is only about $1,000. So you should take the right-hand box only.

The theoretical interest of this problem arises from the fact that two orthodox methods of decision theory give opposite results. How should we deal with this question? The matter is still controversial, but for the present I wish to point out a certain analogy with the position of someone who (a) believes that he or she is one of the saved and (b) would be prevented from crimes only by the fear of hell fire. (I concede of course that most Calvinists would probably have had sufficient natural motivation to virtuous conduct or what they regarded as such.) Because he or she denies the doctrine of salvation by works, the Calvinist I have in mind will not think that his or her subsequent deeds have any effect on his or her final destiny. The analogue of this in the Newcomb Problem is that choosing one or the other of the boxes will not affect the money in the boxes: according to the story it is there already. If the Calvinist has any doubts of his or her salvation by the grace of God, and if he or she thinks that the effects of grace are good works, he or she will feel more confident of having previously received the grace of God and this will give pleasure. Thus any tendency to do good works, however minimal, will continually be receiving positive reinforcement. Many of these 'good works' will be such as we would from a secular point of view regard as virtuous. (Of course we may not regard some as virtuous. Consider for example Calvin's support for the execution of the heretical Servetus. Many of the characteristics that the Scottish Covenanters regarded as virtues are repellent to most of us today, but nevertheless their fanaticisms were not self-regarding, and their courage in pursuing fanatical activity may well have been at least partly due to the sort of psychological mechanism I have just been suggesting.)

Effectively, belief in predestination was a species of fatalism. To return now to my contention that a strong metaphysical sense of the reality of the future is needed for correct thinking about the arms race. Mutual nuclear annihilation might destroy the evolution of intelligence on earth and thus have (negative) consequences indefinitely into the future, so that we must think in terms not only of hundreds or thousands of years, but in terms of millions of years or hundreds of millions of years. We may of course be comforted in thinking of the possibility of annihilation even of all intelligent life on earth by the thought of intelligence having evolved on planets of distant stars, in our galaxy or in the innumerable other galaxies. As intelligent creatures we may not be alone in the universe. As I reported in chapter 1, there is some controversy about the probability of extra-terrestrial intelligent life: some cosmologists regard this as a practical certainty, while others think that the evolution of life required so many happy accidents each of great antecedent improbability that we may well be on our own. Considering the vastness of the cosmos I would guess myself that we are not alone, but that our nearest neighbours might be too far away for communication to be possible. The vast distances might explain the lack of contact with extra-terrestrials. After all, if extra-terrestrial life is as common as some cosmologists believe, it is probable that much of it will be technologically far in advance of us. Even a few centuries is nothing cosmically, but in the history of technological civilization it is huge. Another more sinister thought, that has been suggested to explain our apparent lack of contact with extra-terrestrial intelligent life, is that when civilizations reach the sophistication needed to make atomic bombs they invariably destroy themselves.

In some of the stories in John Buchan's novel mentioned earlier in this chapter the chief protagonist believes that he *knows* of some event in the future, but tries hard and unavailingly to do things that would prevent this event. This is irrational. Or at least it would be if this belief that he knew the future amounted to certainty. Knowledge implies truth. The trouble with the fatalist is that the fatalist does not know the proposition '*p*' about the future. All the fatalist knows is that either it is true that *p* or that it is false that *p*. Quietism or despair is not indicated. There is not the requisite knowledge of the future to make the decision making paradoxical. Our actions causally determine the future. The fact that there are tenselessly true (but often unknown) propositions about the future does not imply fatalism, or encourage either quietism or despair. But even if fatalism were true, the psychological mechanism that I have discussed could well prevent such quietism or despair. It is a question for empirical investigation as to which are the most likely to inhibit moral seriousness about the future, (1) the confusions that lead to questioning the reality of the future or (2) the confusions that lead to fatalism. Perhaps such an investigation could be made by social psychologists, though it may be that only philosophers with good metaphysical insights will easily see the importance of it.

### SUGGESTIONS FOR FURTHER READING AND
### BIBLIOGRAPHICAL REFERENCES

For discussions of the problem of free will see R. L. Franklin, *Freewill and Determinism: a study of rival conceptions of man*

(London: Routledge & Kegan Paul, 1968); T. Honderich (ed.), *Essays of Freedom of Action* (London: Routledge & Kegan Paul, 1973); D. C. Dennett, *Elbow Room: the varieties of free will worth wanting* (Cambridge: Mass.: MIT Press, 1984); and Galen Strawson, *Freedom and Belief* Oxford: Oxford University Press, 1986). For a more detailed and technical statement of the line taken in the present chapter, see J. J. C. Smart, *Ethics, Persuasion and Truth* (London: Routledge & Kegan Paul, 1984), chapter 7. The paper by R. E. Hobart mentioned in the chapter is 'Free Will as Involving Determinism and Inconceivable Without It', *Mind, 43* (1934), 1–27. That by C. A. Campbell is 'Is "Freewill" a Pseudo-Problem?', *Mind, 60* (1951), 441–65, which was followed up by 'Professor Smart on Free-Will, Praise and Blame: A Reply', *Mind, 72* (1963), 400–5. This Reply was to J. J. C. Smart, 'Free-Will, Praise and Blame', *Mind, 70* (1961), 291–306. For problems about the exact definition of determinism and whether the common belief that classical physics is deterministic is correct, see John Earman, *A Primer on Determinism* (Dordrecht: Reidel, 1986), and 'Why Space is not a substance', *Pacific Philosophical Quarterly, 67* (1986), 225–44.

Richard Taylor's argument for fatalism can be found in Richard Taylor, *Metaphysics*, 2nd edn (Englewood Cliffs, NJ: Prentice-Hall, 1974). A useful discussion of fatalism is R. D. Bradley, 'Must the Future Be What It Is Going To Be?' *Mind, 68* (1959), 193–208. There are some remarks about whether we can change the future in A. J. Ayer, 'L'Immutabilité du Passé', *Etudes Philosophiques, 1* (1953), 6–15. For Newcomb's Problem see Robert Nozick, 'Newcomb's Problem and Two Principles of Choice', in Nicholas Rescher (ed.), *Essays in Honor of Carl G. Hempel* (Dordrecht: Reidel, 1969), and Michael D. Resnik, *Choices: an introduction to decision theory* (Minneapolis: University of Minnesota Press, 1987), pp. 109 ff. For Calvin on predestination, see John Calvin, *Concerning the Eternal Predestination of God*, translated with an introduction by J. K. S. Reid (London: James Clarke, 1961). Michael D. Resnik, *Choices*, op. cit., pp. 112ff, relates Newcomb's Problem to Calvinism and predestination. On the Reality of the Future, see the essay on that subject in J. J. C. Smart, *Essays Metaphysical and Moral* (Oxford: Basil Blackwell, 1987), originally published in *Philosophia, 10* (1981), 141–50. See also A. N. Prior, *Papers in Logic and Ethics* (London: Duckworth, 1976), chapter 11, 'It Was To Be'.

# 7

# God and Cosmology

## A DIVINE CREATOR OR ARCHITECT?

In chapter 4 I gave a passing mention to the sort of argument for the existence of God used by Paley, who said that just as a watch required a watchmaker, so the universe required a God who designed it. (In fact this argument was stated in ancient times by Cicero in his *De Natura Deorum*.) This argument, the Teleological Argument or Argument to a Purposive Designer, was in Paley's hands considerably concerned with the adaptedness of living creatures and their organs, such as the human eye. Darwin's theory of natural selection weakened this argument because it suggested that these adaptations and appearances of design could be explained naturalistically. However, theologians did not give up the general form of the argument. They stressed not particular cases of biological adaptedness but the wonderful beauty of the universe at large, and the intricacies and yet simplicities of the law of physics.

David Hume, in his posthumously published *Dialogues Concerning Natural Religion*, gave the classic criticism of this sort of argument. He pointed out that the comparison of the universe to (say) a watch and of God to a watchmaker was a weak one. Perhaps other analogies could be stronger. Could one not with more plausibility argue that the universe was more like an organism? *Prima facie* animals and plants are generated *without* being designed. In this respect they are not like artefacts. Furthermore, if the analogy is meant to give us an argument for a Divine *Creator* it will not do at all. *At most* it is an argument for a divine architect or designer, who imposes design on already existing material. A watchmaker does not create a watch *ex nihilo*.

It might be thought that if God planned the universe then there must be as much complexity in the plan as in the universe itself, and as much complexity in God's ability to *make* the plan. Of course much complexity and apparent designedness can arise by natural selection. A simple plan for creating complex life forms might be to create a planet suitable for life and ensure that proto-life exists on it, and let natural selection do the rest. (Or perhaps very many such planets, since complex life on earth may have arisen as a result of a succession of improbable lucky accidents.) But we are not here concerned with the design of species of living organism but with the laws of nature themselves. Now if God invented the laws of nature there must have been complexity in *him*. So there would be as much need to explain the complexity of God as that of the universe. (A point made by Hume.)

It has been said by a certain sort of theist that God is not a concrete entity but an abstract principle. Contemporarily, this is said very interestingly by the Canadian philosopher John Leslie, but Leslie traces the idea back to Plotinus and the Neoplatonists. He believes that his idea is consistent not only with the obscure utterances of Protestant theologians such as Paul Tillich who identify God with 'the ground of our being' but also with those Catholic theologians who employ the doctrine of Analogy to say that calling God a Person (or three Persons) is not to say that he is a concrete entity like an ordinary person. (The analogy is supposed to lie elsewhere.) Leslie calls his position 'extreme axiarchism' and he identifies God with an axiarchic principle: the principle that value tends to come into existence. He points out that when we say that something ought to be the case we are taken to be asserting that it is good that it should. He extends this common idea to the assertion that the axiarchic principle is *creative*: the universe exists because it is good that it should. Also he holds that only consciousness has intrinsic value or disvalue. So the axiarchic principle is supposed to explain not only that the universe exists but that a universe with consciousness in it exists. Though conscious robots might conceivably be invented in the future, hitherto consciousness seems to be associated with carbon based life. Indeed even if they were self-reproducing the robots themselves would have come into being only through carbon based intelligent beings that made the first generation of them. Carbon based life depends on the formation of galaxies, then stars, then planets. (According to modern cosmology.) Now the possibility of galaxies, let alone stars, planets and carbon based life, depends on an extra-ordinary fine tuning of the constants of nature. This has been discussed a great deal by recent cosmologists. Moreover, the argument would be unaffected if the possibility of other chemical bases of life was considered, for example silicon based life evolving near the surfaces of stars. There would still be fine tuning needed for the evolution of stars.

### MULTIPLE UNIVERSES AND COSMIC ACCIDENTS

These coincidences, some of which I shall mention in a moment, are so striking and of such extreme antecedent improbability (or so it would seem) that they have cried out for explanation. Some of these explanations are from the so-called anthropic principle, which needs to be combined with a theory of an ensemble of small 'u' universes within the all-embracing big 'U' Universe of everything that there is. This ensemble of small 'u' universes can be either postulated outright, as was done by Brandon Carter, or made independently plausible, as in the theory of the 'inflationary universe' as proposed by A. Guth and others. According to this theory the early universe expanded or 'inflated' at a truly mind-boggling rate. The general idea has been developed by A. D. Linde in a new way, on whose popular account in the *New Scientist* (7 March 1985), as well as some summaries by John

Leslie, I have to rely. Guth and Linde postulated a huge exponential expansion from a tiny volume (perhaps $10^{-33}$ cu.cm) at the time of the 'big bang' from which the universe originated. According to Linde this expansion was by a factor of $10^{1,000,000}$, a truly amazingly large number. This expansion is meant to explain the extraordinary smoothness of space-time. The turbulence arising from the big bang would not otherwise lead us to expect such smoothness. This huge expansion would smooth away any initial turbulence. The theory implies that the big 'U' Universe, of which what we think of as our universe is a tiny or even infinitesimal part, will assume on an immensely huge scale something like the crystal structure of a metal, each crystal being a small 'u' universe. (Linde's analogy.) At the 'crystal' boundaries there will be turbulence, a great 'roughness' of space-time, but the small 'u' universes are so immense that this does not affect anything within the range of our observation. The theory also predicts that the proto-laws of the very early universe developed into laws of the same mathematical form in all the small 'u' universes but with randomly different values of the constants. In only a very small minority of the small 'u' universes will be constants be such as to allow for the evolution of galaxies, stars, planets and carbon based life. Naturally, since we exist, carbon based life, planets, stars and galaxies exist, and we must be in one of the small 'u' universes with the lucky values of the fundamental constants. This is an application of the so-called 'anthropic principle' in cosmology. There is said to be an 'anthropic selection effect'. The term 'selection' here is a bit metaphorical. We don't select the small 'u' universe that we inhabit. To use an example of John Leslie's, suppose that a million prisoners are tied to a million trees and that each of them is individually shot at by one of a million machine guns. Suppose that it is probable that about one of the million machine guns will miss the target. A prisoner who thus survives may think himself lucky, and he knows that it is he who survives because he's still there to ask the question, though he did not himself select his tree.

Nevertheless, the thought that a million such incidents were occurring and that there was a statistical probability that one or more prisoners would be lucky, gives some sort of explanation of the fact that he is still alive.

It is not important for the philosophical purposes of the present book to worry too much about what the lucky coincidences are, but I shall mention a few of them just to show that they are antecedently very improbable ones and so very striking. One of them is the relation between the gravitational coupling constant and the fine structure constant which determines the strength of electromagnetism. As Brandon Carter pointed out, if gravitation were very very slightly weaker, or electromagnetism were only very slightly stronger, all main sequences stars (of which our Sun is a typical example) would be red dwarfs, and if gravitation were very slightly stronger or electromagnetism very slightly weaker, all main sequence stars would be blue giants.

And here we are talking of variations possibly of the order of $1:10^{40}$ – fine tuning with a vengeance. An even more extraordinary piece of fine tuning is needed to account for the smoothness of space-time. As was already noted the theory of inflation was designed to explain this smoothness, but the inflation itself apparently requires a piece of truly extraordinary fine tuning, where two components of the cosmological constant (which accounts for expansion of the Universe against the attractive force of gravitation) must cancel one another with an accuracy of at least $1 : 10^{50}$. Such numbers are mind boggling. Without the smoothness of space-time there would have been such turbulence that galaxies could not have formed, still less stars and planets. Similarly there is a flatness problem. If space-time were not almost quite flat the very early universe would have recollapsed before galaxies could form or else would have expanded too fast for galaxies to form. This involves a fine tuning of $1 : 10^{55}$, but would be explained also by inflation, which as noted already itself requires very fine tuning.

There are also reasons why there has to be fine tuning of

the ratio between the nuclear weak force and the nuclear strong force if a universe like ours with galaxies and stars could evolve, or even for all hydrogen not to have burned to helium.

The energy density of the universe is critical. If there had been slightly more density the universe would have contracted back early on and there would have been no time for galaxies, still less stars, to have formed. If there had been less density the universe would have expanded so fast that particles would have been too far apart for them to condense into galaxies. This delicate balance may depend on the mass of the neutrino. Until recently it was thought to have zero mass, like the photon, but it is now thought to have a mass of less than a millionth of that of the electron. Despite this very small mass the total mass of all the neutrinos in the universe could outweigh that of all the stars, since there are believed to be something of the order of $10^9$ of them for every cubic metre throughout space.

In the previous pages I have been indebted to some of the writings of John Leslie. Leslie has collected a list of about one hundred coincidences possibly necessary for intelligent life on earth to have evolved, though some, as he concedes, are less impressive than others. Just what all the coincidences are does not matter for the philosophical argument to follow.

## THEISTIC AND NON-THEISTIC ATTEMPTS TO EXPLAIN THE OSTENSIBLE COINCIDENCES

As was suggested a couple of pages back, when I mentioned John Leslie's analogy of the many prisoners, the ostensible fine tuning of our (small 'u') universe may be explained by the postulation of many small 'u' universes, as by Brandon Carter, or by the hypothesis, made on independent grounds, of the inflationary (big 'U') Universe which comes to contain within it a large number of small 'u' universes, each with different values of the relevant fundamental constants of nature. We don't just say 'How fortunate the fine tuning' and leave it at that. (Note that I follow Leslie and others in using the terms 'fine tuning' so as not to imply that there was a Fine Tuner.) We say 'With all the randomly different small "u" universes, a few will be fine tuned, and since we are here to tell the tale it is obvious that a life-permitting universe is the sort of universe that we're in.' This is a use of the so-called Anthropic Principle in Cosmology, proposed by Brandon Carter. In connection with the hypothesis or postulation of many small 'u' universes it does seem to be genuinely explanatory. Notice that I have here said '*ostensible* fine tuning'. On the many-universe hypothesis, there was no actual fine tuning, as by a Divine Technician. There were the randomly varying small 'u' universes of which a few were likely to be fit for evolution of galaxies, stars, carbon based life and intelligence.

We must not get the wrong idea from the word 'Anthropic' here. The theory is not anthropocentric, as was the Ptolemaic account of the solar system. We could also talk of Galactic or Stellar Principles: since in only a few of the small 'u' universes would galaxies or stars exist, and since we observe that galaxies and stars *do* exist, obviously we must be in one of the small 'u' universes that permit the evolution of stars and galaxies. For any such explanation to be genuinely explanatory, it needs to be combined with the idea of many small 'u' universes.

Contrast illegitimate forms of anthropic reasoning. A good many years ago G. J. Whitrow attempted to explain the three-dimensionality of space (or the four-dimensionality of space–time, one might say) as follows. He made use of a mathematical theorem to the effect that in classical mechanics and gravitational theory planets could not have stable orbits if space had more than three dimensions. This theorem makes the independently plausible assumption that gravitational force in an $n$-dimensional space varies over distance as the inverse $(n-1)$th power of the distance. (In three dimensions we get the Newtonian inverse square law.) Whitrow also used the premiss that intelligent life could not exist except on a planet with a stable orbit. (This premiss might be questioned, but it would be to stray from my main argument to question it here.) Whitrow also has an argument, of a very odd sort, in order to show that the number of dimensions of space cannot be *less* than three. He makes use of the fact that only in a space of three or more dimensions could there be a complicated neural network, and with no brains there would be no minds to formulate the problem.

It can readily be seen that Whitrow's explanation is preposterously back to front. It is the three-dimensionality of space that explains (or partially explains) the stable orbits, the nerve nets and the existence of minds which can formulate the problem, and not vice versa. Whitrow was not writing in the context of a theory of multiple small 'u' universes. If there were multiple universes of course some of them (not ours) could have other than three-dimensional space.

Without the hypothesis of many small 'u' universes the anthropic 'explanations' of the fine tuning of the constants of nature, discussed in the last few pages, would be equally preposterous and back to front. The fine tuning explains (or partially explains) the existence of galaxies, stars, planets, carbon based life and minds that can formulate the problem, but these things do not explain the fine tuning. With the hypothesis of many small 'u' universes we do get something that has claims to be a genuine explanation of the fine tuning. Note also that complex neural networks (and hence minds) are not the only things that are explained (or partially explained) by the three-dimensionality of space. In consequence I think that there may be idealist or Kantian elements in Whitrow's thought.

It should not be thought that the back to front 'explanations' of Whitrow and others are without interest. I shall begin with two more examples. John Lucas has called the above-mentioned argument the 'high-don' argument because it concerns the more cerebral activites of Oxford college high tables. He also considers a 'hi-fi' argument and what he calls a 'low-don' argument, because it is concerned with the less intellectual activities of eating and drinking. (Lucas attributes the latter argument to Whitrow.) Take the hi-fi argument first. Because of a mathematical argument due to Richard Courant it can be shown that only in a space of three dimensions can electromagnetic or other waves transmit sharply defined signals. Since such communication does exist we can deduce from this fact that space has three dimensions.

Similarly it may seem obvious that eating and drinking is not possible in a space of two dimensions, because in such a space an alimentary canal would not exist – try to make such a canal and you divide an organism into two separate ones. I see loopholes, since in some way there might be attractive and repulsive forces between halves of a sufficiently exotic organism so as to hold the two halves just the right distance apart, but in so far as this argument is cogent one can deduce from the activity of eating and drinking that space has more than two dimensions. But this does not explain the more than two dimensions of space: it is the other way round. Of course this 'low-don' example is trivial, though the 'hi-fi' argument has a little more theoretical interest.

In the case of the fine tuning there is more interest. Even though, in the absence of a theory of multiple universes, the argument is not explanatory and is back to front, nevertheless it is of interest that one can predict certain facts of fine tuning from facts about our familiar world. The preposterousness of Whitrow's arguments and similar arguments comes from their being put forward as explanatory. As *predictive* (or retrodictive) of facts about certain constants of nature in the early universe they are quite sensible. The fact that we know what these constants are (at least assuming that they have not changed over time) does not deprive the argument of interest, since it makes connections between apparently unrelated facts.

THEISM

At the beginning of this chapter I considered theistic explanations of the fine tuning of the universe. I then passed on to considering theories of multiple small 'u' universes which give a secular explanation. Outright postulation of such a 'universe' ensemble may seem ontologically prodigal, but the theory of inflation provides independent reason for believing in such prodigality. Of course such theories are highly speculative and may not stand the test of time. But, then, equally the theistic hypothesis is highly speculative too, and there have been plenty of philosophers who believe that they can refute it. In recent times one of these has been John Mackie, whose book *The Miracle of Theism* examines arguments for the existence of God. The argument that Mackie seems to treat with the greatest respect, even though without final acceptance, is that of John Leslie, already mentioned in this chapter. Leslie is also very sympathetic to theories of multiple universes and in particular of inflation, and so he is torn both ways, though I think that his predominant inclination is towards theistic explanation. It will be recalled that Leslie's conception of God is not that of a concrete entity but that of an abstract 'axiarchic' principle. As was noted, Leslie claims support for such an abstract conception of God in certain Protestant and Catholic theologians and in Neoplatonic philosophy. Whether this theory really deserves the appellation 'theism' could be contested by the ordinary Christian, Muslim or Jewish believer. Can one pray to an abstract principle? Can an abstract principle answer prayers? Will an abstract principle greet the martyr in paradise? The theologian's and philosopher's concept of God is presumably an esoteric one, but Leslie could be happy enough about that: in science the esoteric can be true, and why not also in theology?

Leslie's theory (of 'extreme axiarchism') is a complex and subtle one, but the main idea, it will be recalled, is that there is an axiarchic principle that value tends to come into existence. Since, according to Leslie, value resides only in consciousness, a universe which permits consciousness to exist comes into existence. Since the fine tuning is necessary for consciousness to emerge the fine tuning of the constants of nature is ensured by the axiarchic principle.

Leslie's principle seems to fail to explain the complexity of the universe. Why all the deserts and empty stellar spaces and why the thousands of millions of years of lifeless plasmas, gas clouds, stars and early galaxies? If consciousness is all that has value, why does the universe not consist entirely of immaterial spirits? Leslie indeed feels this sort of objection, because in one chapter of his book *Value and Existence* he tries to tame the vast lifeless spaces and times by defending the metaphysical theory of phenomenalism, which I have rejected in chapter 5. In any case, even if phenomenalism were accepted, it would still not account for the apparently unnecessary complexity of the universe. Why the quarks and galaxies and black holes and so on *even if* these are no more than phenomenalist constructions out of sense data? Why not a happy Leibnizian world of immaterial souls or 'monads'? And would such a world of monads need the fine tuning we believe our universe to have? Leslie would say 'yes', that there must be a world with physical laws (this being taken in a sense compatible with his phenomenalism). At least in a phenomenalist sense, he wants to say that a world with matter in it (e.g. so that he could go rock climbing) would be better than a world of pure spirit. While sympathizing with this, one wonders why the axiarchic principle could not have brought into being monads that want only intellectual pleasures. But here I am getting subjectivist about value, which Leslie is not and cannot be consistently with his theory. This brings me on to the considerations of the next paragraph.

Like Mackie, and unlike Leslie, I do not believe that the world contains objective values. Putting it a little crudely, I regard talk of values as an expression of our attitudes, our likes and dislikes. But this is a big subject that would take us into the foundations of moral philosophy, and I shall not press the matter here. Nor shall I discuss whether it is an objection to Leslie's position that not only good but evil has come into existence. This is of course also an objection to other forms of theism. (Leslie does attempt to solve this problem in his *Value and Existence*.)

### DOES THE FINE TUNING REALLY NEED EXPLANATION?

Do we need either a theory of many small 'u' universes or a theistic explanation for the fine tuning of the early universe? Some philosophers will contend that no explanation whatever is needed. They will say that the constants of nature must have some values or other. So why not the fortunate ones? After all, any particular sequence of fortunate values will be *a priori* no less improbable than any particular sequence of unfortunate ones.

There seems to be a fallacy here. Given a particular unfortunate sequence, this would require explanation, no less than a particular fortunate one. What would not require explanation would be that there was some unfortunate sequence or other. This does not need explanation because the set of unfortunate sequences is hugely greater than the set of fortunate ones. (I say 'greater' here rather than 'more numerous', because however narrow the ranges of fortunate values there could be an infinity of values of them, and so according to set theory the set of fortunate values could be equinumerous with the set of unfortunate ones. But a *measure* of the latter set might be very much greater than a *measure* of the former one.)

Of course the fortunate sequence might have a greater *posterior* probability relative to a sufficiently plausible non-probabilistic explanation. Consider cards numbered 1, 2, 3 . . . 100 that have been well shuffled in a machine. After further shuffling the cards come out in the order (1, 2, 3 . . . 100). We can think of a purpose for a sequence of cards ordered in this way, and so if we observed such a thing we might suppose, for example, that someone had tampered with the shuffling machine. With a sequence such as (17, 80, 31, 52, . . . 64) we could think that the sequence had fallen out by chance, despite its low probability.

The moral of this is that though the initial probability of a salient sequence is no greater than that of a non-salient sequence we may easily conjecture some hypothesis to explain the salient sequence, relative to which the probability will be raised. We may look for a purposive explanation, which would be an analogue of a teleological or axiarchic explanation of the fortunate coincidences relating to the constants of nature.

The same sort of conclusion can arise from the hypothesis of many small 'u' universes. Recall John Leslie's example of the many prisoners each being individually shot at by a single machine gun. One out of a million prisoners survives. This prisoner will feel fortunate, but will think his good fortune sufficiently explained by the reflection that it is likely that one of the million machine guns will probably miss the target. Since he is there to think of it he is obviously the lucky one. Here the 'many machine gun' hypothesis does not seem to be redundant, provided it is combined with the prisoner's reflection that he is alive to tell the tale. So also with the many small 'u' universe hypothesis.

WHY DOES ANYTHING EXIST AT ALL?

Whether or not theism can explain the fine tuning of the universe, it does not seem to me to be able to explain why anything exists at all. The simplest universe would be the null universe. So in some moods the question 'Why does anything exist at all?' does seem to me, as to many other philosophers, to be the profoundest of all questions, while nevertheless it seems obvious that it could not possibly have an answer.

As has been noted, the traditional teleological argument for the existence of God could at best be an argument to a great Architect, not to a Creator. Is the case better with Leslie's extreme axiarchism? The axiarchic principle is the principle that value tends to come into existence. So perhaps the axiarchic principle is supposed to explain the existence of the universe. Waiving my reservations about Leslie's theory, let me ask the question: 'What about the axiarchic principle itself?' It is easy to forget that a *principle* (whatever a principle is) is itself an entity of some sort. If it is felt to be mysterious that the universe exists, why should it not be felt equally mysterious that the principle itself exists? To explain why I make this point, I must say something about the concept of a 'law' or 'principle'.

Sometimes when we see the word 'law' in a book of physics, what seems to be indicated are certain law *sentences* in the book. The same perhaps is true of 'principle'. Clearly this interpretation would not do for 'axiarchic principle'. Or consider Leslie's own expression 'axiarchic requirement'. A law, principle or requirement cannot plausibly be thought to be a sentence. How could a sentence bring anything into existence or fine tune a universe? Even if it could, it would have to exist antecedently to the universe. Perhaps a law, principle or requirement is a *proposition*, some timeless Platonic entity. Or it might be, as some philosophers have contended, a relation between universals. But then the problem recurs: 'Why should Platonic entities or relations or universals exist?' seems as baffling as 'Why should the universe exist?' Leslie's own position seems to be that the axiarchic principle is a necessary proposition, and so we do not need to explain its existence. I have three comments to make on this. (1) I am in any case unhappy about the metaphysical notion of necessity involved. I understand only the mundane notions of possibility and necessity which correspond to 'may' and 'must' – you must come or it must rain if your coming or its raining follow by logic from contextually agreed background assumptions. (If you like you can count logical truths as necessary, since they follow from themselves, but the axiarchic principle hardly seems to be a truth of logic. There is no contradiction deducible from its denial.) The problem of possibility is the same as the problem of necessity, since 'it is possible that' is equivalent to 'it is not necessary that not'. (2) The previous point of course is controversial among philosophers. Some philosophers hold that a proposition is necessary if it is true in all possible worlds. This leaves us with an ontology of possible worlds other than the actual world, and so we have even more to worry about, not only why the actual world exists but also why the possible worlds exist. (3) Waiving these points, and allowing the axiarchic principle to be necessary, this necessity would be an attribute of its truth, not of its existence as a Platonic object.

In short, the difficulty I feel over Leslie's in many ways exciting and admirable theory is that any explanation of the universe's existence surely presupposes the existence of something whose existence would be as mysterious as that of the universe itself. A similar objection applies to an ingenious and instructive suggestion by the physicist Edward P. Tryon.

Tryon suggested that the universe may have arisen as a vacuum fluctuation. For simplicity I shall have to forget about the distinction between a small 'u' universe and the big 'U' universe. The universe contains a huge amount of mass energy which is positive. (The famous equation $E = mc^2$ expresses the identity of mass and energy.) This mass energy is due to the mass of the various particles in the universe and the fundamental forces between them, other than the force of gravitation. Gravitational energy is negative, and there is an enormous amount of that too. What if the positive energy and the negative energy were exactly to cancel each other out? Suppose that the universe began as a vacuum with no energy at all. Tryon argued that mass and energy could arise, through a loophole provided by Heisenberg's (misleadingly named) uncertainty principle, which we met with in chapter 3, where we considered the principle that momentum and position are conjugate so that if one is determinate the other is indeterminate, and both of course can be indeterminate.

Thus if $\triangle x$ is indeterminacy of position in the direction of the $x$-axis and $\triangle p_x$ is indeterminacy of momentum in the same direction, $\triangle x . \triangle p_x$ is of the order of magnitude of $h$, Planck's constant. There is a similar indeterminacy with respect to energy and time, so that $\triangle E . \triangle t$ is of the order of magnitude of $h$, where $\triangle E$ is indeterminacy of energy and $\triangle t$ is indeterminacy of time.

Now if the total energy of the universe is zero, due to (positive) mass energy and (negative) gravitational energy cancelling out, then for the universe $\triangle E$ could be set to zero and $\triangle t$ would then be infinite. Or if $\triangle E$ is sufficiently near to zero $\triangle t$ can be very large. So perhaps our universe arose spontaneously in this way, with its great mass energy but with zero or near to zero total energy, and with great time span.

Tryon's idea is a very pretty one. However (not surprisingly) it does not answer the philosopher's question 'Why should there be anything at all?' It assumes a structured space-time and the quantum field, and why should there be that? It assumes the existence of laws of nature, and what are these? As we have seen, laws might be thought of as propositions or as relations between universals, and so we might still ask why propositions or universals exist. I myself think of laws as cosmic regularities, but then for these to exist there must be the cosmos to exhibit the regularities.

It is important to note that Tryon is concerned with a temporal beginning of the universe. The philosophical problem is concerned rather with the existence of the universe as a space-time entity. Whether time had a beginning or whether space-time had a singularity at its beginning are questions about the topology of space-time, given its (tenseless) existence. (Recall chapter 2.) Space-time might have a topology a bit like the two-dimensional surface of an idealized pear, with a point singularity at one end of it. Or it might be like (. . . −3, −2, −1, 0, 1, 2, 3 . . .) and have no beginning or end. Or it might be cyclical as with the internal telephone number of my one-time secretary, which was 2341 and which I remembered because of its cyclic equivalence to the easily remembered 1234. Or it might be like (. . . $\frac{1}{16}$, $\frac{1}{8}$, $\frac{1}{4}$, $\frac{1}{2}$, 1, 2, 4, 8, . . .) having no beginning but being almost as if it had one. And so on. All these possibilities are neutral with respect to our ability or otherwise to explain the existence of space–time thought of tenselessly.

St Thomas Aquinas appreciated this point in his presentation of the so-called Cosmological Argument for the existence of God. The argument is that some contingent (non-necessary) being exists, for example the paper on which I write this. This paper had a cause: events in the paper mill, which had various causes, going back to the cutting down of trees. The trees had causes. And so on. The argument assumes that there must be a first cause which must be something non-contingent, something necessary. However, Aquinas allowed the possibility that the sequence of causes might go back infinitely far in time, so that there would be no temporally first cause. Still, he thought that there would have to be an atemporal first cause, the cause of the sequence as a whole. And this cause would have to be a necessary being, or otherwise the original question would recur: 'Why does it exist?'

The main difficulty about Aquinas' argument resides in the notion of a necessary being, of which I can make no sense that would help the argument. I think that Aquinas would agree that 'necessary' cannot mean 'logically necessary', so that there is nothing self-contradictory in atheism. Indeed there is an argument, the Ontological Argument, for the existence of God that is closely connected with the idea that denying God's existence would be self-contradictory, and Aquinas rejected this argument. One suggestion about 'necessary' here is 'requiring nothing else for its existence'. The idea is that the universe could not have existed without God, but that God could have existed without the (created) universe. But why should the universe require anything outside itself for its own existence? If the universe required God for its own existence, why should God not require something else for his existence? That is, we could ask the child's good question, 'Who made God?' (Also if God created the laws of nature he must be of at least equal complexity and so we would be no nearer a simple explanation.) In the absence of a suitable account of a clear and appropriate sense in which God could be said to be a necessary being, a sense in which the universe itself could not be such a being, the cosmological argument is unconvincing. I think it unlikely that such a sense of 'necessity' will be forthcoming.

In this chapter we have come to the verge of great mysteries. But some at least can be the subject of rational speculation. Whether in my naturalistic philosophy there is room for genuine mysticism is another matter. I *feel* it with the question 'Why is there anything at all?' even though it seems impossible that the question should ever have an answer. What is it that I (and a good many other philosophers) feel, and how is the feeling to be explained psychologically? Is the feeling something to be cherished, or is it one that should be explained away, just as in earlier chapters I suggested that the feeling that time flows and the feeling of the ineffability of consciousness should be explained away?

### SUGGESTIONS FOR FURTHER READING AND
### BIBLIOGRAPHICAL REFERENCES

The best contemporary defence of traditional theism is perhaps in Richard Swinburne, *The Existence of God* (Oxford: Clarendon Press, 1979). The best contemporary critique of theism is J. L. Mackie, *The Miracle of Theism* (Oxford: Clarendon Press, 1982). For Aquinas' cosmological argument for the existence of God and criticism of it, see Donald R. Burrill (ed.), *The Cosmological Arguments: a spectrum of opinion* (Garden City, NY: Doubleday, 1967). A very comprehensive survey of contemporary cosmology is the massive volume by J. D. Barrow and F. J. Tipler, *The Anthropic Cosmological Principle* (Oxford: Clarendon Press, 1986).

John Leslie, *Value and Existence* (Oxford: Basil Blackwell, 1979) is sympathetically discussed by Mackie in *The Miracle of Theism*, op. cit., and Leslie replies to Mackie in his paper 'Mackie on Neoplatonism's "Replacement for God"', *Religious Studies*, 22 (1986), 325–42. Leslie has written many papers on cosmology in connection with his axiarchism and with the anthropic principle. Some of these are: 'Anthropic Principle, World Ensemble, Design', *American Philosophical Quarterly*, 19 (1982), 141–51; 'Observership in Cosmology', *Mind*, 92 (1983), 573–9; 'Modern Cosmology and the Creation of Life', in E. McMullin (ed.), *Evolution and Creation* (Notre Dame, Ind.: University of Notre Dame Press, 1985); and 'How to Draw Conclusions from a Fine Tuned Cosmos', Vatican Observatory, forthcoming. See also John Leslie (edited with Introduction), *Physical Cosmology and Philosophy* (New York: Macmillan, forthcoming). This book contains essays by authors with various points of view.

Other references are: P. C. W. Davies, *The Accidental Universe* (Cambridge: Cambridge University Press, 1982); G. J. Whitrow, *The Structure and Evolution of the Universe* (London: Hutchinson, 1959), and 'Why Physical Space has Three Dimensions', *British Journal for the Philosophy of Science*, 6 (1955–6), 13–31; J. R. Lucas, *Treatise on Time and Space* (London: Methuen, 1973), especially §48; J. J. C. Smart, 'Philosophical Problems of Cosmology', *Revue Internationale de Philosophie*, 41 (1987), 112–25; Brandon Carter, 'Large Number Coincidences and the Anthropic Principle in Cosmology', in M. S. Longair (ed.), *Confrontation of Cosmological Theories with Observational Data* (Dordrecht: Reidel, 1974), pp. 291–8; Edward P. Tryon, 'Is the Universe a Vacuum Fluctuation?', *Nature*, 246 (1973), 396–7; C. E. Mortensen, 'Explaining Existence', *Canadian Journal of Philosophy*, 16 (1986), 713–22; Nicholas Rescher, *The Riddle of Existence* (Lanham, Md: University Press of America, 1984); Quentin Smith, 'World Ensemble Explanations', *Pacific Philosophical Quarterly*, 67 (1986), 73–86; Ian Hacking, 'The Inverse Gambler's Fallacy: the Argument from Design. The Anthropic Principle Applied to Wheeler Universes', *Mind*, 96 (1987), 331–40; John Leslie, 'No Inverse Gambler's Fallacy in Cosmology', *Mind*, 97 (1988), 269–72; Jonathan Katz, 'Why There is Something: the Anthropic Principle and Improbable Events', *Dialogue*, 27 (1988), 111–20.

# 8

# Metaphysical Realism

I have taken it that it is from science that we learn about the nature of the universe. Towards the end of chapter 1 I touched on the Kantian view that our knowledge is only of a 'phenomenal' world, and that this world is not a world of things as they are but of things as shaped by the fundamental constitution of our minds, by the so-called 'categories'. Kant thought that there were things in themselves, about which we could know nothing, because to know them would be to know them as structured by our minds, not as they are intrinsically. Later philosophers rejected the things in themselves: if nothing could be said about them why should we suppose that they exist and what meaning is there even in asserting that they exist? After all, if we say that $\phi$'s exist (e.g. 'unicorns exist') we are saying that the predicate '$\phi$' applies to something. (For example, that '. . . is a unicorn' applies to something.) But if no predicates can be asserted true of things in themselves, in what sense can we say that they exist? Unless, perhaps, the predicate '. . . is a thing in itself' can be asserted true of them, but this in itself contradicts the Kantian position in that our notion of a thing in itself would then be infected with the categories, and so if something in itself is a thing in itself, then it is not a thing in itself. By *reductio* it would appear to follow that there are no things in themselves.

By parity of argument, however, the very meaningfulness of this negative statement could itself be questioned.

Some German critics of Kant identified the thing in itself with the phenomenal object, the object as shaped by the categories of the mind. After all, it might be said nowadays that if through evolutionary natural selection our minds have come to order things in certain ways (e.g. in terms of the Kantian categories of substance and causality) this may be because the world, as it is in itself, is a world of substances acting causally on one another. It could then be objected that this assumes that useful theories are true. It may be useful to think in terms of substance and causality in the ordinary concerns of life that were important to our prehistoric and pre-human ancestors, but this does not imply that things really are like this. Nevertheless, it could be said that usefulness implies *approximate* truth. Euclidean methods are useful for surveyors and navigators, even though we may hold that space is not really Euclidean. This is because in the local region of ordinary human application space is approximately Euclidean. (Kant held that not only the categories but geometry was imposed on the world by our mental constitution.) Just as we can rise above a rigid adherence to Euclidean geometry, so in quantum mechanics we can rise above and reject the category of causality.

Perhaps, however, the Kantian theory might be thought of as asserting that certain categories (structural principles of thought) have been 'hard wired' into our brains as a result of natural selection. This is very plausible. Noam Chomsky has indeed argued that certain very deep principles of grammar are hard wired into us and he also holds that without this hard wiring it would be impossible for a child ever to learn its mother tongue. We do not need to commit ourselves to this Chomskyan view: it is enough to note that at least it has a certain plausibility. However, just as Euclidean geometry is better than non-Euclidean for everyday purposes, because it is simple and good enough for what we need, why could we not say that although the 'hard wiring' of the Kantian categories would have a practical advantage over alternatives, nevertheless this makes a theory of the world in terms of these categories at best approximately true? For example, the category of causality works well on the macro-level but not on the micro-level. This need not prevent us from identifying the phenomenal objects with noumenal ones. The phenomenal descriptions might be strictly false of the noumenal objects but nevertheless *approximately* true of them.

According to Kant science deals with the phenomenal world, not the metaphysically real world of things in themselves or 'noumena'. Or if the interpretation of 'things in themselves' as identical with the phenomenal things is correct, science does deal with the noumena but not *as* noumena: they are known in what is a metaphysically illusory way. Nevertheless, the things in the phenomenal world are not illusory in the *ordinary* sense: we can still make, at the phenomenal level, the distinctions between mirages and real lakes, sticks looking bent when half in water and sticks really being straight, and so on.

I propose to dwell a little on two ways of understanding Kant's distinction between phenomena and noumena. One is that noumena and phenomena are distinct. For example, an electron may be a phenomenon (part of the phenomenal world) but distinct from things in themselves. Perhaps a thing in itself could be paired with it, perhaps not. I'm not clear enough about the notion of things in themselves. Perhaps we may be *inclined* to say that no particular thing in itself could be paired with an electron, because then we *could* say something about the thing in itself, namely that it was paired with a certain electron (e.g. the electron that was responsible for a certain cloud chamber track). But even if it would have seemed to make sense to Kant to talk of pairing a thing in itself with an electron, he would not have allowed us to say that there was a *causal* relation between a noumenon and a phenomenon. This is because causality is a category and things in themselves are supposed to be independent of the categories. Kant seemed to think that if we had to talk in terms of our innate categories about noumena, this would make the noumena mind dependent and so part of the phenomenal world.

Now consider the other interpretation of Kant, namely that an electron could be identical with a thing in itself, but *as* noumenon it would not have the property of being an electron. This seems to go against the logical law of identity, that if $x$ is identical with $y$, then any predicate true of $y$ is true of $x$. If the professor of anatomy is identical with the dean of the medical faculty, and if the dean of the medical faculty is bald and rides a bicycle, then the professor of anatomy is bald and rides a bicycle. Indeed the phrase '*as* noumenon' that I have just used is far from clear. In my example of the identity of the professor of anatomy who is bald and rides a bicycle and (unknown to us) is dean of the medical faculty, it would be odd to say that *as* dean of the medical faculty he or she did not ride a bicycle, though *as* professor of anatomy he or she did do so.

To go further into this matter, let me explain a term much used by philosophers, namely the term 'natural kind'. Electrons and protons are natural kinds, because there are laws such as that any electron has an electric charge equal and opposite to that of any proton. On the other hand, let us consider the class of things that are either electrons or archbishops or dustbins. This does not seem to be a class that is the extension of any predicate that functions essentially in an important law sentence. Of course we could point to such a sentence as 'All electrons, archbishops and dustbins have mass.' Nevertheless, we can consider not just one law but a whole cluster of laws in which the predicate 'is an electron' figures, which shows that the concept of an electron 'cleaves reality at its joints', whereas this is not the case with 'is a boojum' (where to be a boojum is to be an electron, an archbishop or a dustbin): there is no such cluster of laws relating to boojums, so that the concept of a boojum in no way 'cleaves reality at its joints'.

Now we might identify the professor of anatomy at a

certain university with the dean of the medical faculty. And we might identify the professor of biochemistry at a second university with the dean of the faculty of medicine. At a third university we might identify the professor of biochemistry with the dean of the faculty of science. (For simplicity I am assuming the old-time one-professor departments throughout!) So there are individual identities but not law-like ones as there would be if in all universities the professor of anatomy was *ex officio* dean of the medical faculty. As was remarked in chapter 5 philosophers commonly call the former sort of identity a 'token–token' identity and the latter sort of identity of 'type–type' one. So perhaps we should interpret Kant as supposing a 'token–token' identity between phenomena and noumena. That is, the ultimately (metaphysically) true laws about the real world, the laws about noumena, are supposed to be unknowable by us. A given electron may be identical with a given noumenon $X$ but the class of electrons would not be identical with any noumenal natural kind to which $X$ belongs. The noumenal laws would not carve reality at the same joints as the phenomenal laws do. I do not think that Kant would have accepted this interpretation, because he would probably have argued that in talking of laws relating to noumena carving nature at the joints I am already bringing the noumena under the categories. Probably the theory of phenomena and noumena cannot be made completely consistent. I am concerned, however, to make as much sense of it as I can, even if only to reject it.

According to this interpretation, phenomena are identical with noumena, but the laws of phenomena are quite different from the laws of noumena. You may ask 'How can the laws of noumena be different from those of phenomena if phenomena are identical with noumena?' Does this not conflict with the logical law of identity which I mentioned earlier? I need here to introduce the distinction between intensional and extensional contexts. Is not this cheating? Should we not reject the law? To this I say 'no'. I would argue that intensional contexts are only *apparently* intensional.

(Recall chapter 4.) Consider the sentence 'I want to meet the professor of anatomy.' Here 'I want to meet' is an intensional context. I may want to meet the professor of anatomy because I believe that he or she is a bush walker. I do not want to meet the dean of the medical faculty because I (perhaps) believe that the dean of the medical faculty is someone with a pathological hatred of philosophers. Apparently the law of identity does not apply in expressions with certain contexts, in this case the context 'I want to meet . . .'. The surface grammar of 'I want to meet the professor of anatomy' is misleading.

Now I assert that the context 'the laws of' is an intensional (or apparently intensional) context. To talk of the laws of phenomena is to talk of law-like sentences expressible in the phenomenal vocabulary. Or perhaps, if you believe in properties it is to talk of relations between phenomenal properties. So the law of identity does not conflict with the statement that the laws of noumena are different from the laws of phenomena. It is still obscure, however, how we could meaningfully talk of laws of noumena at all.

I am afraid that my attempt to do the best for Kant's distinction between phenomena and noumena (things in themselves) may have led us into obscurity and even perhaps more confusion than before. It might have been better to have said at the outset that the phenomenal world is the one real world. Of course this was the line taken in the idealist tradition after Kant, but the idealists unfortunately characterized the world as mind dependent or partly mind dependent. I do not want to say of course that we have got the phenomenal world exactly right. We may have to revise some of our views about electrons, for example, just as atoms are no longer thought of as indivisible or as truly atomic. I do want to claim that despite future theory change much of what we say now about electrons will still be assented to, and in this sense the predicate 'is an electron' will still be approximately true of the same entities of which we now assert it to be true.

Kant thought that the phenomenal world was mind

dependent because we could not avoid imposing on experience certain categories and certain forms of spatial and temporal intuition. However, 'mind' in 'mind dependent' here refers to a 'transcendental' non-empirical self, not to the empirical mind investigated by psychologists. Psychology is a science like any other and so informed by the categories.

From my naturalistic point of view Kant's distinction between the transcendental and empirical selves looks obscurantist. So let us look at the matter naturalistically, and let the categories and forms of intuition have to do with the empirical self (which I identify with the brain). It is a matter for empirical evidence and theorizing as to whether the human brain contains certain innate categories, forms of intuition or principles of intellectual organization. Thus, is our perception of space as three-dimensional and approximately Euclidean learned or it is determined by an innate programming of our brains? Well, let us for the sake of argument grant an affirmative answer to the second half of this question. This is quite plausible in view of evolutionary considerations. It does not show that to organize experience in a way shaped by these categories and forms of intuition is not truly to represent the world as it is, independently of mind. (Unless we are representing minds, of course.) Or at least, approximately as it is. Surely common sense beliefs, at least if they are purged of theological and magical accretions, must in the main be approximately true. If they guided our ancestors through the world, so that they avoided being eaten by wild beasts, and so that they were able to hunt and gather food, make fire, seek out caves, and so on, there must have been a correspondence between their beliefs and the real world, and if innate categories and so on enabled our ancestors to achieve this correspondence and find their way about in the world this in no way implies that the real world is at all mind dependent.

We would not expect an *exact* correspondence between the real world and our implicit and perhaps partly 'wired in' theories about the world. Approximate truth is what is needed for survival. It is plausible that whether innately by learning or both, the brain of a tiger has something on the lines of Newtonian kinematics set up in it. So do we, as is testified by our ability to get our heads out of the way of fast cricket balls. It is not something of which we are consciously aware, but the required theoretical information must be registered appropriately in our brains. The most comprehensive metaphysically correct theory need not be the most useful in practice: it would be impossible to use the general theory of relativity to calculate the nautical almanac. So even if there is innate programming in our brains, this does not mean that we cannot kick our ladder away after we have ascended it. Perhaps thinking in terms of Kantian categories of substance and causality may have been good for our survival as a species, but having survived, human beings may invent theories such as quantum mechanics which do not seem to be informed by the Kantian categories.

### IS THERE A ONE REAL WORLD?

When I assert that the phenomenal world is the metaphysically real world, this must be taken as 'by and large'. Most of our scientific beliefs today are true or approximately true. I do not want of course to deny that there are vast oceans of truth yet to discover, and that in some respects the universe may trick us. I want to distinguish truth from warranted assertibility even in the limit of ideal theory. The universe may trick us, so that the most reasonable theory may be false in certain important respects. But on pain of pragmatic paradox I cannot say this of a body of core and non-contentious science, since it is in terms of consistency with this core science that the 'may' in 'may trick us' has to be elucidated. But more of this hereafter.

In discussing Kant's things in themselves I toyed with two different interpretations, one according to which phenomena were identical with them and one according to which they were distinct. I adopted the former interpretation. The distinction between laws of phenomena and laws of noumena was invoked to allow a token–token identification of phenomena and noumena. In identifying these I took the possibility of doing so as unproblematic. Hilary Putnam, in several books and articles, in effect has argued with great subtlety against the uniqueness of such an identification. More exactly, he denies the existence of the one real (noumenal) world by arguing that there would be no non-arbitrary ways of assigning reference to the terms of our theories, or to put it in the Kantian terminology of the previous pages, there would be no unique correspondence between phenomena and noumena. Nevertheless, though Putnam thinks that talk of a noumenal world leads to inconsistencies, he has expressed some sympathy for the urge to postulate such a transcendental world. In the end I think that we must interpret him as holding that the noumenal world drops out altogether, talk of it making no sense. Accordingly we must see him as rejecting the idea that phenomenal objects can be identified with noumenal ones.

It will be recalled that Kant did not regard the phenomenal world as illusory. He makes a distinction between appearance and reality *within* the phenomenal world. Atoms, for Kant, would not be like ghosts or mirages or things that appear to us in dreams. If realism is merely a matter of making *this* contrast, it is what Putnam calls 'Internal Realism'. Putnam's arguments are very subtle and sometimes technical, but we can sum up his conclusions from these arguments as follows: If there were a noumenal world, then there would be no non-arbitrary way of pairing phenomenal and noumenal objects, and so phenomenal objects cannot be identical with noumenal ones, and so there is not a one real world, as envisaged by the metaphysical realist. Thus Putnam argues, in a novel way, different from Kant's, that phenomenal reality is partly mind dependent. When I use the adjective 'phenomenal' here I am of course alluding to Kant. Putnam denies the intelligibility of noumenal reality and according to him phenomenal reality is the only reality that there is. According to Putnam the idea of a mind independent world is an illegitimate one. As Putnam has put it metaphorically on page xi of his *Reason, Truth and History*: 'the mind and the world jointly make up the mind and the world.'

How is the connection set up between a name and what it names? Or again, how is the connection set up between a predicate and the class of things to which it applies? There is no way in which a consistent set of sentences uniquely determines the things and classes of things to which the names and predicates of the sentences apply. This is so even if the set of sentences is infinite, as is the case with the set of consequences of the axioms of a theory. Another example of a consistent set of sentences is the set of true sentences of a language. We may not know which sentences are in these sets, in the former case because of the difficulty of finding proofs and in the latter case, of knowing which sentences are the true ones. An intriguing example of the thesis that reference cannot be determined internally comes from the Skolem–Löwenheim theorem in logic. This theorem was used by Putnam in one of his arguments against metaphysical realism, though he has used less technical arguments also. The Skolem–Löwenheim theorem says that any consistent set of sentences, whether finite or infinite, has a model in the arithmetic of the natural numbers. So consider any theory such as thermodynamics, theology, or whatever, expressed in the framework of first order logic (the logic of the truth functional connectives, and the quantifiers 'there is a . . .' and 'for any . . .', and variables $x$, $y$, $z$, . . . and predicate letters 'F', 'G', 'H', . . ., etc. and identity, which I am assuming to be adequate for science and metaphysics). Then this theory can be interpreted as about the natural numbers (0, 1, 2, 3, . . .). Clearly this is a non-standard model of thermodynamics or of theology, but how do we distinguish standard from non-standard models? Or is everything relative to our arbitrary choice? To say 'yes' to this would be to embrace idealism with a vengeance. (Not the subjective idealism of Berkeley but something more like the objective idealism descending from Kant to the neo-Hegelians.)

It is a slight diversion from my concerns in this chapter, but interesting in itself and perhaps useful here for illustrative purposes, but I shall here mention the so-called Skolem paradox. George Cantor defined two sets as equinumerous if they can be put in one–one correspondence. Thus without counting we can tell that the set of husbands in a room (in a monogamous society) is equinumerous with the set of wives in the room. If sets are finite, they cannot be equinumerous with proper parts of themselves. This is not so with infinite sets. Thus the set of even numbers is equinumerous with the set of all the natural numbers: we can marry off $n$ with $2n$ for every $n$.

Indeed we can define an infinite set as one that can be put in one–one correspondence with a proper part of itself. Cantor showed that the set of natural numbers was equinumerous with the rational numbers (numbers $m/n$ where $m$ and $n$ are positive or negative integers) but that the set of real numbers (which include the irrational numbers such as $\sqrt{2}$ and the transcendental numbers such as $e$ and $\pi$) was larger than the set of natural numbers or of rational numbers. The set theory in which this can be proved is axiomatizable in first order logic. So by the Skolem–Löwenheim theorem it can be modelled in the natural numbers, even though in its standard interpretation it asserts the existence of sets greater than the set of natural numbers.

Skolem's paradox may be thought of as what Quine has called a 'veridical' paradox, surprising but true. After a time such a paradox can come to be regarded as platitudinous. At any rate it vividly illustrates how an infinite set of sentences is not able to determine reference from within. How is the standard model of set theory distinguished from non-standard models? This is not the whole story, but it is in part due to the way in which set theory is integrated into our wider language, as when we say that *Mansfield Park* is a member of the set of Jane Austen's novels.

This only postpones the problem of answering Putnam's challenge. How do we fix the reference of the wider, common sense language, in which set theory is embedded? Any consistent set of sentences in this language will have non-standard interpretations too. How do we know whether we are talking about all the things we think we talk about, stars, planets, people, ships and shoes and sealing wax, and not, for example, the natural numbers? Does this question have no answer so that we cannot speak of an objective real world, or does it have an answer and if so what is the answer?

The answer seems to lie, in part, in our causal interactions with the world. For example, I may learn to refer to someone as 'Tom' by hearing sentences containing this name with Tom in the vicinity, and light rays coming from Tom into my eyes, and so on. Similarly with predicates. Of course this does not by itself enable me to know whether 'Tom' refers to the full four-dimensional entity Tom or (say) a temporal stage of Tom. Language has to be learned somewhat holistically, and in particular this depends on one's grasp of the concept of identity. Two different temporal stages may be parts of the *same* entity Tom throughout time but not the *same* temporal stage. I do not wish to advocate a full causal theory of reference, but wish to say merely that causal interaction with the one real world is part of the story of how reference (or a standard model) is established.

Putnam's reply to such a move is that the causal story is just more theory. Add this story on to our set of true sentences and we can apply the argument about reference all over again. How can we say that the word 'cause' uniquely refers to causes? And so on.

The dialectical situation is such that we seem to win on even-numbered occasions and Putnam seems to win on odd-numbered occasions. Or at least at first he may seem to. I would urge, however, that his challenges are uncalled for. We may know how to refer without having a theory of how we do it. In fact this is the case for all except a few philosophers. We can refer uniquely to an objective real world, even though the set of sentences we use has non-standard models. (Just as one can ride a bicycle without having a theory of how we do it.)

Or again, consider Lewis Carroll's instructive paradox 'What the Tortoise said to Achilles'. The Tortoise refuses to accept that 'All *A*'s are *C*'s' follows from 'All *A*'s are *B*'s' and 'All *B*'s are *C*'s'. He says that it does not follow unless Achilles puts in the premiss 'If all *A*'s are *B*'s and all *B*'s are *C*'s then all *A*'s are *C*'s', but when Achilles puts in this premiss the Tortoise says that he needs yet another premiss: If all *A*'s are *B*'s and all *B*'s are *C*'s and if all *A*'s are *B*'s and all *B*'s are *C*'s then all *A*'s are *C*'s, then all *A*'s are *C*'s'. Clearly this can go on for ever. The Tortoise keeps wanting to replace the rule of the inference by an additional premiss, and then of course another rule of inference is needed . . . . Indeed it is possible to reason correctly without knowing the rules of inference one uses, and a centipede would trip up and be unable to walk if it were to state to itself how it moved its legs. The distinction I have in mind is Gilbert Ryle's distinction between 'knowing how' and 'knowing that'.

Similarly we may have the ability to refer uniquely, even though it is the case that if we converted this 'know how' into 'know that' we would still be left with a set of premises without a unique interpretation. It is true that any ability is explicable by means of a piece of knowing that, but however comprehensive our discourse there will be a piece of knowing how unexplained. *Any* piece of knowing how can be explained but every piece cannot be explained, since the last explanation will always come as a result of a piece of knowing how.

Now if we produce a theory of reference and incorporate it in our total system of the world, Putnam can indeed ask how we are so sure that this total system refers to a unique mind independent reality. If we always allowed this challenge we might as well say that if any claim to sureness had to be backed up by a further sureness, then we could never be sure of *anything*. The theory of reference is not all that much a specially difficult case.

Tentatively, then, this is the sort of way in which I would answer Putnam's challenge. Reference is a special case of intentionality, and Ruth Millikan has pointed out that intentionality always lies partly outside of consciousness. (Just as knowing how cannot be entirely reduced to knowing that.) Though our reference depends on our thoughts, the success of reference requires the existence of theory independent objects: as Millikan remarks, theory independent objects are the only objects there are anyway. I am not suggesting that Putnam himself makes this mistake, but it may be worth pointing out that it is easy to slip from talking of an $X$ to talking of the concept of $X$-ness. We must not confuse our concept of a thing with the thing itself. Nevertheless, though the thing itself is independent of our theories, if these theories are good ones our concept of a thing may perfectly well apply to that theory independent entity. Electrons exist independently of our theories about them, but predicates belonging to our theoretical discourse (e.g. 'has a negative electric charge') may well be true of them.

### TRUTH V. WARRANTED ASSERTIBILITY

If we want to have a full-blooded theory of a world independent of minds (except in so far as it *contains* minds, among other things) we must have a full-blooded theory of truth, in which truth comes out as correspondence with reality, or something like it. Truth must be distinguished from warranted assertibility, even in the limit of a perfect science. The great American philosopher C. S. Peirce identified truth with warranted assertibility in the limit. (The phrase 'warranted assertibility' itself comes, I believe, from John Dewey, another influential American philosopher in the past.) Of course it is obvious that a person may be warranted in believing that something is true when it is not true. All the evidence may indicate that a prisoner is guilty, and may be sufficient for a court to convict the defendant, but nevertheless the defendant may be innocent. The philosophers who I am opposing will agree with this, of course, but only in the sense that further evidence or further investigation might show the prisoner to be after all innocent. A realist about truth, such as myself, would want to say that even if it were physically possible to get more and more evidence for proposition $p$, and we thus came to be more and more warranted in believing $p$, nevertheless the warranted assertibility of $p$ must still be distinguished from the truth of $p$.

Suppose that we say that there is exactly one tree $x$ metres and $y$ metres respectively from the door knobs of the front doors of the town halls of Rio de Janeiro and São Paulo. Suppose also that unknown to us a tree happens to exist at this position in the Amazonian forest. Suppose also that this tree falls down at precisely noon on 1 January of a certain year. Let the proposition that a tree of this description falls at this time be designated by '$A$'.

On the supposition that I have just made, $A$ is true. And even without the supposition don't we want to assert that either $A$ is true or $A$ is false? Thus won't we allow that the logical principle of bivalence (that a proposition is either true or false) is correct? The anti-realist rejects the principle of bivalence because warranted assertibility does not obey it, and he or she wishes to elucidate truth in terms of warranted assertibility. Certainly there are propositions such that neither they nor their negations are warrantedly assertible: the case of the tree in the Amazonian forest is an example.

Anti-realists of this sort wish to identify truth with some sort of warranted assertibility because they think that no sentence could be understood unless one knew the truth conditions for that individual sentence, and they think of truth conditions as assertibility conditions. They may agree that in *a sense* we understand the sentence about the Amazonian tree in that we understand a subjunctive conditional: we could say what *would* warrant us to assert it (or to deny it) in certain conditions, e.g. if we had been there at the appropriate place and time. Now contrary to fact or subjunctive conditionals are tricky things, and it seems odd to elucidate our understanding of a simple indicative sentence such as *A* in terms of a contrary to fact conditional. Why do we believe the case of the subjunctive conditional? Presumably only because we believe in bivalence of the simple indicatives themselves.

Instead of the Amazonian forest we might consider a universe causally disparate from ours. Thus our macroscopically four-dimensional universe might be a mere four-dimensional cross-section of a macroscopically five-dimensional Universe. (Let us as before spell 'Universe' with a capital 'U' to distinguish it from the sort of thing we normally think of as the universe. 'Universe' with capital 'U' denotes everything.) Then there might be another universe causally unrelated to ours which exists as another four-dimensional cross-section of the total Universe. So it would be physically impossible to get news of this other universe, or even to be warranted in believing that it exists. Yet is not the supposition intelligible? Would not a sentient being, suffering pain perhaps, in that other universe be justifiably miffed at the thought that anti-realists in some other universe (which might be ours) would hold that the proposition that pain exists in an unknown universe had no truth value?

Anti-realists have objected to me that this sort of argument is circular. The anti-realist just would claim not to understand the example. Yet surely it *is* understandable. All we need to understand it is some five-dimensional geometry, and it does not need much mathematics to provide that.

Consider again the tree in the Amazonian forest. The anti-realist holds that it is true that the tree fell at a certain time if and only if it is warrantedly assertible (perhaps in the limit of ideal science) that the tree fell then. But this seems to me to be obviously false. Even in the limit the evidence might point nowhere or in the wrong direction. The anti-realist may reply that I have been using 'if and only if' in the classical sense, so that '*p* if and only if *q*' is true if and only if '*p*' and '*q*' have the same truth value, so that both are true or both are false. The anti-realist models his or her epistemology on so-called intuitionist logic in the philosophy of mathematics. He or she will say that '*p* if and only if *q*' is true only when the warranted assertibility of '*p*' would allow us to warrant the assertibility of '*q*', and vice versa. So the argument of this paragraph, convincing as it may possibly seem at first sight, is not a knock down one against the anti-realist. Nevertheless, the anti-realist may seem to us be committed to a view that is highly far-fetched and unplausible.

One trouble about the anti-realist's position is his or her narrow conception of understanding. We need a more holistic theory of meaning. In my view this is provided by Donald Davidson's truth theoretic approach, based on Tarski's theory of truth. Let me digress for a moment to say something about this.

Tarski's theory is for formalized languages. Davidson's hunch was that the underlying structure of natural languages was based on 'first order predicate logic' (which was the basis of Tarski's formalized languages), and Davidson's interesting research programme is to make it plausible that, certain appearances to the contrary notwithstanding, the underlying structure of natural languages fits this pattern. A language based on first order logic contains (besides names and variables and certain syntactical devices such as parentheses) just three sorts of symbol. (1) Truth functional operators 'and', 'or', 'not' and others definable in terms of these. (2) Primitive predicates. In the case of English, these could be all the verbs and most of the adjectives you would find in the Oxford English Dictionary. But not all: e.g. 'big' is not a predicate but a predicate operator: a big mouse is not big and a mouse, nor is a small elephant small and an elephant. To deal with 'big' in first order language we have to replace 'big mouse' (say) by 'mouse bigger than most mice', or something of the sort. (3) The quantifiers 'For any *x*' and 'There is an *x* such that', (or the same with '*y*', '*z*', etc.). Predicates and open sentences (e.g. '*x* loves *y*') are 'true of' or 'false of': 'red' is true of tomatoes, false of lemons, and '*x* loves *y*' is true of the ordered pair 'John, Mary' if John loves Mary. In fact, for technical reasons Tarski has to use not the simple notion 'true of' but the more complicated notion of a predicate or open sentence being 'satisfied' by a sequence of objects. Tarski also gives satisfaction conditions for the truth functional operators and the quantifiers. Thus the open sentence '$y$ is blue or $x$ is red' is satisfied by any sequence of objects whose second member is blue or whose first member is red. Note that if we order variables ('$x$', '$y$', '$z$', '$w$', '$x''$', '$y''$', '$z''$', '$w''$', . . .) '$y$' comes second and '$x$' comes first. I shall not bother here to state the satisfaction conditions for the quantifiers, which are more complicated.

So far this looks trivial. Tarski gave a definition of truth in terms of satisfaction and he was able to prove such sentences as ' "All ravens are black" is true if and only if all ravens are black.' What is interesting is not the theorem proved (which looks trivial) but the proof of it from primitive truth conditions. To forget this is to miss the main point. Suppose that I write on the blackboard an immensely long sentence expressible in first order logic. Tarski's theory shows how one can determine the truth conditions for it recursively by eventually getting back to a finite set of truth conditions (or more accurately, satisfaction conditions) for the finite number of building blocks of the language, as in (1), (2) and (3) above. This is far from trivial.

Tarski's theory was important in the philosophy of mathematics because he was able to give a precise account of what it is for a sentence in a formally axiomatized system to be true, and to distinguish the notion of truth in mathematics from that of provability. Gödel had shown that for any consistent set of axioms for a theory at least as strong as elementary number theory there are true sentences not provable or disprovable from the set of axioms. Of course if the set of axioms were suitably strengthened a previously unprovable true sentence could be proved, but then there would be some other true sentences not provable from the strengthened axioms. This suggested that even in pure mathematics truth must be distinguished from provability. For those who thought that the notion of truth was too metaphysical and obscure a notion for mathematics, Tarski's theory provided reassurance.

In a Tarski truth theory the axioms (satisfaction conditions for the primitive expressions) come first, and sentences of the form ' "—" if and only if—' (so-called T-sentences) are proved from them. On the other hand, Davidson is concerned with interpretation of a natural language. He identifies T-sentences and then conjectures a truth theory (set of axioms) from which these T-sentences can be derived. The truth theory is supposed to give a theory of meaning for the language. That is, meaning is not given word by word or sentence by sentence, but holistically. Davidson thinks that our understanding of our own language is a matter of our brains internalizing a truth theory, of which normally we are not consciously aware. Thus our understanding of our language is more a 'knowing how' than it is a 'knowing that'.

It might be said that 'snow is white' corresponds to the fact that snow is white. But does the world contain facts as well as things? Wittgenstein in his *Tractatus Logico-Philosophicus* had a correspondence theory in which sentences pictured facts. Unfortunately his theory was not strong enough for mathematics and science, which requires the quantifiers. Wittgeinstein had an account of the quantifiers, in effect a substitutional one in which 'For any $x$, $x$ is red', for example, is true if and only if whatever name '$a$' you substitute for $x$, '$a$ is red' is true. This does not explain how you can say 'All rabbits have burrows' without having names for all, or perhaps any rabbits. There are other objections to Wittgenstein's theory. If we base our theory, as Tarski did, on the notion of satisfaction, we have so-called objectual quantification and what relates language to the world is satisfaction, not picturing. And contrary to Wittgenstein's *Tractatus* we do not need facts in our ontology: we can say that the world contains things but not facts. Neverthless, a Tarski type theory is in the spirit of a correspondence theory.

Traditionally there have been two important theories of truth, the correspondence theory and the coherence theory. Despite the title of Davidson's paper 'A Coherence Theory of Truth and Knowledge', Davidson's theory, related as it is to Tarski's, is near to being a correspondence theory. Coherence theories are good theories not of truth but of warranted assertibility. We are warranted in asserting $p$ if $p$ maximally coheres with (fits into) our web of belief, including beliefs relating to new evidence. Now hypothesizing a truth theory for a language is much like hypothesizing a physical theory. Coherence is a criterion for adopting a theory, i.e. for warranted assertibility, and so it is a criterion for being warranted in accepting a truth theory, i.e. an interpretation, for an unknown language. If Davidson's paper had been entitled 'Truth and a Coherence Theory of Knowledge and Interpretation' the title would have been less misleading.

Davidson explains our understanding of a language holistically in terms of internalizing a Tarski type truth theory for the language. (If new primitive predicates are introduced, as happens, for example, when new scientific concepts, such as that of 'electron', are introduced, we must be regarded as having new language, but for one who interprets the old language the transition to interpreting the new language is presumably a simple matter.) I believe, contrary to anti-realists, such as Dummett, that understanding can be explained holistically on the Davidsonian model, i.e. by reference to truth and recursive truth theories. Indeed Davidson's first important paper in this subject was entitled 'Theories of Meaning and Learnable Languages'. He took it that our ability to learn a language required a recursive ability to understand the meanings of a potentially infinite (or in-definitely large) complex of sentences in terms of the meanings of their simple constituents. Otherwise we would have to have an infinite (or unplausibly large) capacity for learning the meanings of individual sentences. Thus the fact that a language is learnable constitutes strong evidence that it has a recursive theory of meaning, which Davidson thinks of as a theory of truth conditions. (Davidson does not exactly identify meaning with truth conditions but he holds that a truth theory gives us much of what traditional theories of meaning undertook to provide.)

Now from the perspective of a Davidsonian theory of meaning and understanding, an anti-realist's complaint that he or she cannot understand my example of the five-dimensional Universe looks very unplausible. As I said, pretty well all we need to understand it is some five-dimensional geometry, and there is no great difficulty in incorporating a truth theory for this in the truth theory for the English I have been uttering.

My example was of exactly one extra universe besides our familiar one, each being a cross-section of one five-dimensional universe. The embedding in a five-dimensional universe is in fact not necessary for my purposes in the example. There is a certain difficulty, however. Remember the ensemble of universes proposed by Brandon Carter, mentioned in chapter 7. Carter might think that he was warranted in asserting the existence of this ensemble, which would be either infinite or very large in number. Similar remarks apply in connection with the sub-universes of the 'inflationary universe' of Alan Guth, Andrei Linde and others. So it might be said that we are warranted in *disbelieving* in the example, because it is of only *one* extra universe. Well, I agree that we are warranted in disbelieving it anyway. Either Carter's hypothesis is believable, in which case the example does not give enough universes, or it is not believable, in which case Ockham's razor warrants us in disbelieving the example. Nevertheless, the example does seem to be such that it might be true, even though it is rational for us to disbelieve it. (The hypothesis of the example is consistent with the solid core of science – that is how I cash the 'might'.) It seems to be an excess of *hubris* on the part of the anti-realist to deny that truth might outrun and perhaps be inconsistent with even an epistemologically ideal science. If we accept a Davidsonian theory we are in no danger of having to take part in such manifestations of *hubris*. If we clearly distinguish truth from warranted assertibility we can avoid this *hubris*, in keeping with a theme of this book, that our place in the universe is a modest one.

SUGGESTIONS FOR FURTHER READING AND
BIBLIOGRAPHICAL REFERENCES

Immanuel Kant's most important metaphysical views are expressed in his monumental *Critique of Pure Reason*, translated into English by Norman Kemp Smith (London: Macmillan, 1929). For a readable account of Kant's philosophy in general see Roger Scruton, *Kant* (Oxford: Oxford University Press, Past Masters series, 1982) and John Kemp, *The Philosophy of Kant* (Oxford: Clarendon Press, 1968). A simplified summary and commentary, useful to beginning readers, of Kant's *Critique* is M. G. Dickson, *Understanding Kant's Critique of Pure Reason*, published by the author at 412 Seddon House, Barbican, London EC2. For Putnam's various critiques of metaphysical realism see Hilary Putnam, *Reason, Truth and History* (Cambridge: Cambridge University Press, 1981), chapters 2 and 6, *Meaning and the Moral Sciences* (London: Routledge & Kegan Paul, 1978), part 4, *Realism and Reason: philosophical papers*, chapters 1 and 12. An account of the work of Davidson and Dummett may be found in John Passmore, *Recent Philosophers* (London: Duckworth, 1975). Michael Dummett's writings are voluminous and make hard reading. See especially his *Truth and Other Enigmas* (London: Duckworth, 1978). Donald Davidson's main views on truth and meaning are set out in his *Inquiries into Truth and Interpretation* (Oxford: Clarendon Press, 1984). Davidson's paper 'A Coherence Theory of Truth and Knowledge' appeared in E. LePore (ed.), *Truth and Interpretation: perspectives on the philosophy of Donald Davidson* (Oxford: Basil Blackwell, 1986). For Davidson's semantics in its relation to the correspondence theory of truth, see his paper 'True to the Facts', in *Inquiries into Truth and Interpretation*, op. cit.

I have suggested that Dummett and his followers follow in the steps of certain 'objective idealists' of the turn of the century. See J. J. C. Smart, 'Realism v. Idealism', *Philosophy*, *61* (1986), 295–312, reprinted in J. J. C. Smart, *Essays Metaphysical and Moral* (Oxford: Basil Blackwell, 1987).

On knowing how and knowing that see Gilbert Ryle, *The Concept of Mind* (London: Hutchinson, 1949), chapter 2. For Lewis Carroll's 'What the Tortoise said to Achilles' see *The Complete Works of Lewis Carroll*, edited with an Introduction by A. Woollcott (London: Nonesuch Press, 1939). For criticism of Putnam on Metaphysical Realism see Ruth Millikan, 'Metaphysical Anti-Realism', *Mind*, 95 (1986), 417–31, and David Lewis, 'Putnam's Paradox', *Australasian Journal of Philosophy*, 62 (1984), 221–36. A brief criticism of Dummettian anti-realism may be found in M. Devitt and K. Sterelny, *Language and Reality: an introduction to the philosophy of language* (Oxford: Basil Blackwell, 1987), sections 11.3 and 11.4. For Chomsky's view that deep principles of grammar may be innate (hard wired into us) see for example Noam Chomsky, *Language and Mind*, enlarged edition (New York: Harcourt Brace, 1972). For an introduction to the discussion of Chomsky's philosophical ideas, see F. D'Agostino, *Chomsky's System of Ideas* (Oxford: Clarendon Press, 1986), and John Lyons, *Chomsky* (London: Fontana, 1970).

# Index